PULPIT CRICKET
and other stories

PULPIT CRICKET

and other stories

Fergus McKendrick

with illustrations by
Val Biro

WILLOW BOOKS
Collins
8 Grafton Street, London w1
1983

Willow Books
William Collins Sons & Co Ltd
London · Glasgow · Sydney · Auckland
Toronto · Johannesburg

First published 1983
© Fergus McKendrick 1983
Illustrations © Val Biro 1983

McKendrick, H. F.
Pulpit cricket
1. Cricket – Anecdotes, facetiae, satire, etc.
I. Title
796.35'8   GV919

ISBN 0 00 218026 X

Diagrams by Les Robinson
Set in Linotron Ehrhardt by
Rowland Phototypesetting Ltd
Bury St Edmunds, Suffolk
Printed and bound in Great Britain by
Wm Collins Sons & Co Ltd, Glasgow

To Jean

CONTENTS

Pulpit Cricket

I LOST MY FIRST REAL FRIEND and made my first real enemy during a cricket match played in an Edinburgh church on a grey Sunday evening in mid-winter.

Hamish was his name; 'Wee Hamish' to his friends but not to casual acquaintance, for he had a fighting technique closer to the gutters of Leith than the Academic groves nearer Princes Street, and disliked having his small stature noted.

We met when I went to my public school at the age of eleven and were placed in the same dormitory. We were both foreigners, I from Glasgow, and he from Dumfries, so we naturally gravitated together in this heathen city on the Forth. Our friendship was based on good fellowship, deep understanding, mutual benefit and two sterling warm-hearted characters; it lasted ten weeks. Our enmity arose entirely from a minor ambiguity in the Laws of Cricket, and has lasted, so far, thirty-six years.

Apart from two bright oases, Sunday was desert unrelieved in our boarding-school week. In those days, in that place, the Sabbath meant dressing up in your best clothes and praising the Lord by doing nothing. We were not allowed to play on the school field, we were not allowed to listen to the sinful wireless, breakfast was always burnt porridge because the cook was a Wee Free and the housemaster's wife was English. Altogether, the day was dull, gritty, and without pleasure, except for going to church, which was great fun. If you think that implies a commendable religious bent in one so young, you may well be right about the bent, but you are on tricky ground with the commendable, and dead wrong on the religious.

Just after breakfast, sassenach carbon sour in our mouths, we would parade for our weekly issue of pocket money, a libation totalling threepence, always made up meticulously of two pennies, one halfpenny, and two farthings. If I say that we went to church twice on Sunday, and remind you that we were Scottish, you may be able to guess which of the coins were destined for the collection plate.

We were staunch members of the Presbyterian Kirk; staunch in the sense that we didn't really know that any alternative existed – certainly we weren't offered any. The services were interminably dreary, or seemed so to us, but even then I could recognize a certain dour professionalism which I miss in my present southern exile. They were at least efficiently, powerfully, and determinedly dreary, and we got full value for our bawbees – two and a half hours was par for the course. What is more important to this tale, no self-respecting minister would dare offer a sermon lasting a whit less than an hour and a half.

Apart from one joyous hymn (to which our salivary glands responded like Pavlovian dogs, for lunch or high tea lay, heaven-like, just beyond the glad amen), the sermon came last. The proceedings up to that consisted of hymns and psalms sand-wiched between long prayers composed by the minister *extempore*; at least so I was told. For many years I thought (for I had some Latin) that this meant 'dragged out of his past', and being of

[10]

a charitable nature I assumed this implied before he had picked up much of his no doubt considerable education.

During the preliminary proceedings, there was much upping and downing, which was quite enjoyable on a fairly primitive level. The young know instinctively what is good for them, and praying enriches the soul, while singing does wonders for the wind. But there was no doubt that we couldn't get down to anything really serious until the preacher climbed into the pulpit, and it must have gladdened his heart and raised his pious hopes to see our eager faces peering up at him. I am afraid we were not eager for the salvation he was offering.

We were impatient to get going on one of two major Sunday sports. One was and is a traditional pastime wherever the Sabbath is observed with rigour. I refer to what I might call low-intensity sex, though I understand the level has gone up a bit these days. In my time it involved ogling the girls from our sister school who sat in the pews opposite. We never actually met these girls, unless they were in fact our sisters – which didn't count – and probably the boldness of the eye contact was in inverse proportion to the possibility of any other form of contact. However, we didn't understand these things, and consequently enjoyed ourselves enormously.

The other game was pulpit cricket, which as far as I know is limited to England and other nations where cricket proper is taken neat. How we learnt it I cannot remember. That first winter term I had not yet played the real thing in any serious organized way; cricket in the Clyde valley is not a heavy scene, or wasn't then. But somehow we knew the rules, and we played it with solemn intensity, and, as you will see, serious intent. It knocked the blazes out of flirting, which we tended to employ merely to fill out the slack patches inevitable in even the most enthralling of games. I have to admit that as I got older the emphasis changed, but that is another story.

The way we played (there are local variations), was as follows: each of the two players drew up a team, usually of international repute. The selector normally appointed himself captain and opening bat: false modesty was uncommon, although Squiffy MacFarlane frequently put himself No. 7 with Hutton as skipper. We put this down to an unhealthy passion for Denis Compton and prophetic disregard for the eternal values of amateurism. Squiffy grew up to be a Senior Taxation Officer, obsessed with mere cash values, and he still wears Brylcreem.

The captains drew lots, and the winner submitted his team to the whims of the umpire – not the Great Arbiter in the sky, Who was not, we thought, likely to be entirely sympathetic, but His temporal agent, the current preacher, who was innocently and immediately available. His every gesture was scrutinized as a possible sign of divine decision-making – we assumed that the Good Lord knew Umpires' Standard Signalling Technique.

Thus, a hand raised aloft was a bye, unless the finger was pointed, which meant out, and the next man on the list faced up. Horizontal arm-swings were fours, and I well remember a visiting High Churchman who shocked our Elders to their quivering puritan cores with his genuflections, but nearly seduced us into the arms of the Scarlet Woman by blessing the congregation, and thereby clocking up three four-byes on the trot. I have ever since been attracted to religious symbolism.

On the other hand it may be that my bias against red-hot gospelling was instilled by a Salvationist from Inverness who callously destroyed one of my most promising sides in thirty seconds of hectoring finger-wagging diatribe on the evils of strong drink. Wee Hamish insisted that each wag was a wicket, and I had to admit he was within his rights. We remained friends on that occasion, for a sportsman plays by the rules, but I never buy *Watchtower* in a pub.

One arm held horizontally was a no-ball, and during a particularly accusatorial sermon I had to invite Hamish to take Lindwall off for bowling sixteen consecutive bouncers. He was very firm with Ray, but diplomatic, as any great captain must be.

Short runs were very rare, but we had one visiting preacher who kept hitching up his academic hood, and as a result produced a negative score in a Test between England and Scotland: not so unnatural as it sounds, for Scotland was batting.

Other rules I leave to your imagination, for I must come to the break between myself and Wee Hamish. It was the last Sunday of term, and the evening service. We had started the final and deciding match of a series of seventeen two Sundays previously, but play had been deplorably slow, due largely to the fact that the preacher at every service had been the local incumbent, the Rev. Doctor Zebediah MacTavish, MA, DD, whose theology was divine, but scoring rate diabolical. The match had, however, gradually built up to an exciting climactic position as the reverend gentleman lumbered into his peroration. My side (McKendrick's Cricketing Kings – MCK rather than MCC – subtle stuff), had crawled to 46 all out. Hamish's lot (some idiot name like Toppsex – a bit obsessional, was Hamish) had clawed their way to 41 for nine. It was riveting. It had been riveting for over twenty minutes while the diverse pieces of the sermon were pinned together with great dialectical skill but no sporting significance.

'Amen,' cried the preacher.

Oh no! Not a tame draw after four arduous sessions in the field?

Now came the friendship-shattering event. Some great upsurge of religious fervour seized the normally undemonstrative minister. He flung both hands high towards heaven, and cried again.

'Amen, Amen!'

He stepped back, and fell off the pulpit with an enormous crash.

To some present the immediate question was whether the preacher was damaged: rather more had the same worry about the pulpit, for ministers are two a penny, but repairs cost hard cash. For us, there was only one issue: was it a six, or had he quitted the field of play before completing the signal?

We could not agree, Hamish and I, and the argument twisted and finally killed our once happy relationship. I got a letter from him the other day. It began: 'Dear Sir or Madam.' Perhaps we never knew each other all that well.

Promenade Cricket
(or Blood on the Sand)

SCARLET ARTERIAL BLOOD froths on the sun-drenched skin.

She senses it, feels the luscious luke-warm liquidity of it trickling between her bronzed shoulder-blades.

Her soft hand, long fingers tipped with a different shade of red, moves tentatively, searchingly, behind her.

Contact.

The bubbling, oozing sensation between skin and skin.

The hand withdrawn; observed.

The scream! The dreadful scream!

So ended a potentially great cricket match on the promenade at Gass, on the Windshire coast, under a blazing sun in late July 1940. Its disastrous conclusion bears out well that oft-repeated dictum, 'Never try and take an easy catch with one hand.' But let me tell you the whole story . . .

I was a proud and successful member of what was generally accepted to be the best side in those parts, recruited exclusively from the beach-huts between 'Sea-Horses' and 'Gin-and-Tonic'. Since the latter was just next to the tea-and-ice-cream kiosk run by Mrs Kettlewell, the limitation was subtly more than arbitrary, for beyond the kiosk the beach-huts were owned by the Corporation, and let out on short rentals of as little as a week at a time. Further down, near the pier, so it was rumoured, you could hire a hut for a day, but none of us ever went down that far, so had never observed the dreadful things that might be packed into a short lease and a tiny bathing-machine.

There was a time-factor involved in qualification too. The first year you were tolerated as a close spectator at matches and might be allowed to fetch a ball hit into the sea. In your second year nobody objected if you volunteered for full-time fielding on the beach-hut boundary. This was the least popular beat, as it involved scrabbling among the debris under the huts when one got through the mid-wicket field and (very dicey, this) asking Mrs Kettlewell for the ball back if someone pulled a leg-spinner over mid-on from the swimming-pool end. You also had to avoid tripping over Billie Tait's Granny, but this was a physical rather than an emotional hazard, for old Mrs Tait was totally inert, and balls and boys bounced off her all day without producing any response except the recurring argument over whether or not she counted as part of the field of play. Much later in my career I played on a village ground in deepest Bedfordshire which had an oak tree in exactly the same place as Granny Tait; it was much older, bigger, and more beautiful than she, but it caused exactly the same argument when hit by a ball.

By the third summer you might well be accepted as a full member of the team, depending on wastage at the top end. That in turn depended largely on hormones, which in those days didn't seem to act so early or as catastrophically as they do now. I suspect that the age of onset of puberty varies directly with the average area of cloth used in bathing-costumes, but which is cause and which effect I hesitate to define.

At any rate, it meant that people stayed on in our team until almost pensionable, or so it seemed to the young hopefuls on the

[15]

fringe waiting for Full Status. A fellow's eighth birthday could come and go in the flash that is life without a hint of recognition.

I was awarded the accolade in the middle of my second season. This was partly a sort of inverted nepotism, for my elder brother provided the vacancy by falling madly in love with Heather MacLugg of 'Western Fancy'. It was a short-lived romance; she jilted him for the brave lad who helped Mrs Kettlewell sell ice-cream, though whether for his bravery or his ice-cream was never seriously in doubt – more than armies march on their stomachs. I met Heather again recently after a gap of nearly forty years; six children and presumably many, many ice-creams had given her a stomach two or three armies could manoeuvre on, never mind march.

The Team would not have my brother back; he was a Fallen Man. It was generally accepted as a Dire Warning to me, and in later years I paid it no attention whatsoever, with predictable and highly enjoyable results.

The early promotion proved fully justified. Within two seasons, by the age of nine, I was known along almost the entire length of a good one-third of the beach for my devastating Chinaman. Since I am right-handed, there were two sources of error in this reputation. One was terminological; in that distant outpost of the game, pre-television, we used technical words with a child-like lack of interest in their true meaning matched only by that shown by present-day journalists in their use of most of the rest.

The other was a large crack in the surface of the promenade, on a good length, just outside the off stump at the kiosk end. I developed a knack of dropping soaring dolly-drops into this fault, which turned the ball practically at right angles. I suppose I thought all cricket pitches had such convenient pot-holes, or that it was something I did with the ball which caused it to leap about like a demented yo-yo. Later experience sadly disabused me of these notions; in more senior cricket I was called up to bowl only if the captain didn't know me, or was me. But at least I recognize with fellow-feeling, though for somewhat different reasons, the look of sadistic anticipation on a Test-team off-spinner's face as he watches his long-legged, left-handed, fast-bowling colleague manufacturing just such a jagged basin ideally placed for his later bowling from the other end.

My downfall resulted from Rank, and the privileges that go with it. With seniority came the right to field permanently at fine leg/mid-off. Just behind this not very deep position was a steep step up to the next level of promenade, so no ball ever got far past the fielder there, except for skiers, and they were six-and-out, thus to be retrieved at contemptuous leisure. Furthermore, a firmly-struck ground shot often bounced back off the step, and sometimes hit the wicket. Local rules deemed the step to be an extension of the fielder, and credit for a run-out, if so achieved, redounded on him.

Fielding there was normally a profitable sinecure, and with hindsight I must admit I got slack; there is no doubt that one cannot field at peak efficiency with a bottle of Tizer in one's left hand and an iced lolly in the right.

We were moving towards the climax of a needle match of more than cricketing significance. There is a naïve view of sport which claims that it must never be tainted by politics. I learned even at that tender age that this is impossible; games are won and lost, and this involves the assertion of dominance. The pecking-order thus established is inevitably reflected off the field, often in matters of considerably greater import, as in this case.

Our opponents were our neighbours to the North, representing beach-huts 'Lazidays' to 'Restawhile' inclusive. These included a block of four belonging to the Grand Promenade Hotel, which caused bad feeling since their occupants tended to be fly-by-night short stay guests and so, by our standards, strongly suspect. However, their Dads poured large drinks into our Dads, and their Mums retailed much juicy hotel gossip to our Mums, so the pressure on us was irresistible – we had to play them.

The political matter adding edge to this encounter was the *de jure* control over the local station platform. We had it *de facto*, but infiltration had become recently more than accidental. On the platform was a slot-machine vending single De Reske cigarettes at a peñny a go, a plum territorial asset which we could not allow any alien group to exploit. A too-rapidly emptying machine might arouse official, and then parental, interest. As usual, that would simply convert the mildly and enjoyably naughty into the traumatically and boringly wicked.

We had to win.

When my story begins, we had declared at 3,427 for 15, and they were struggling in reply at 1,843 for 12. (These scores are understandable if you realize that the promenade was only 16 feet wide, and some 12 feet above the sands – a stroke which got through to the beach was worth at least eight runs, as the nearest fielders raced to the steps, battled their way down against the ascending tide of migratory adults, leapt across, and often on, the blistering bodies, persuaded the inevitable huge friendly dog to release the ball, and returned it to the keeper via a relay of throwers which always included Henry Figgin's little sister – who was absolutely *hopeless*.)

Their opening batsman, who wore a single wicket-keeper's glove, and was therefore rated of semi-professional status, was still there on 751. Their number 13 was a rabbit, and he was facing. They were, in fact, in an even more parlous state than this suggests, for two of their best batsmen, held in reserve as was the custom in beach cricket, and yet to bat, had just been summoned peremptorily in to tea. Thus, if we could get one more wicket down before their mothers released them, (with luck, a good fifteen minutes – it was high tea in those parts), they would lose by default.

The rabbit swung wildly, ballooning a swirling skier to the right of deep mid-off.

Me.

I rushed to get under it, overcoming my greed enough to drop the iced lolly, but unable to crack my conditioning sufficiently to release the bottle of Tizer.

The ball soared out over the edge of the promenade. I tried to reach it with my right hand, while holding the bottle upright in my left.

The problems of balance proved too great. I tripped and fell, half over the edge overhanging the beach. The bottle shattered on the concrete, my left hand among the pieces. One sliver of glass sliced painlessly into the tip of a finger, deeply enough to nick a small artery. I lay face down, and as in the slow motion of a dream, watched the bright blood mingle with the fizzy lemonade, roll towards the edge, and over.

I poked my head out beyond the lip, and saw below me a lady of ample proportions, on her front, a vast expanse of naked back exposed to the sun and, now, to the drips from above.

This is where you came in, and it was where we got out – very fast. Match abandoned; pressure of Public Opinion. I still carry the scars.

It was Mrs Kettlewell.

French Cricket

It is a sad but incontrovertible fact of life that apparently innocent pastimes can be instruments of corruption and degradation, and it is my unpleasant duty to admit that there is one version of our Great National Sport in this category. Just as our Puritan fore-fathers found the guileless glimpse of an artless ankle led to thoughts of higher things which were uplifting in a reprehensible way, so a trivial type of childish cricket can, in my experience, lead a lad along a pernicious path no mother would wish his fair feet to follow.

I refer to the branch of the game whose name is the title of this tale, which I feel bound to relate as a caution to all parents. Watch carefully what your children do at play: unless rigorously moni-tored it can lead to disaster in adult life. I certainly blame my father for the two great social defects which have blighted my maturity. Paternal supervision at the critical instant could have ensured that I would be able to knot a tie in such a way that it did not within fifteen minutes resemble an extra-laryngeal umbilicus. It would also have ensured that too much right hand did not always convert my cover-drives to long-on pulls, nor my long irons to massively out-of-bounds slices. I have cunningly avoided the latter pitfall with my own son by forcing him to bat left-handed; he drives sweetly, but stutters abominably. The former problem does not arise since, when he does wear a tie, the knot tends to be in roughly the correct position for an umbilicus.

French Cricket is played by one player defending his shins with his bat while another, or others, try to strike them with a ball. It is usually played with a tennis ball and is, in fact, more fun that way, but it is very exciting when a proper cricket ball is used, and in this form is listed in some encyclopaedias as a blood-sport.

A batsman who is hit on the toes is also out, but this is considered by the cognoscenti to be an inferior type of dismissal; accepted gracefully, of course, for a Gentleman does not carp when the small print of the Rules of Life turns out to be somewhat petty. A bowler who knows how these things are does not accept credit for such a victory, just as in the big game he would not claim merit for a run-out at his end if he got a finger to a hard drive and, coincidentally, it hit the stumps. There are batsmen who hold much the same view of lbw but this is generally considered to constitute a rather exaggerated notion of what is meant by small print.

In my part of the world, the French Cricket world was rent by a schism much more profound than that which separated our Roman Catholic and Protestant parents. After all, they were only on about things like who got the best jobs, the new houses, the political handouts; we were arguing about matters of Faith and Belief – about Religion in a pure sense of the word.

There were two sects: the Stickers, in Kitchener Street, and the Jumpers, in Roberts Street. The Stickers (that was us) held that once a batsman had taken his stance he could not thereafter move his feet. The Jumpers allowed that he could switch position if he had struck the ball with the bat. This enabled him to turn completely to face the likely direction of the next ball, instead of having to twist his body round while leaving his feet anchored, as under our rule.

They thought us rigid and unyielding in the face of the realities of human anatomy; we considered their whole approach bordering on the effete. They laughed at our contortions; we taunted their leader, Bobby Gorbelly, whose rotund shape was probably the underlying political reason for their permissive attitude to this essentially moral question. We held fast to the doctrine that fashionable flexibility leads to lascivious licence, and quoted as proof the rumour that up near the High School there was a group of teachers' children who allowed the batsman to wear shin-pads. That way a person could avoid the natural consequences of his voluntary actions, and then what price Accountability?

Both groups despised the Haig Street lot, a bunch of chicken-hearted leftist liberals, who allowed movement of the feet if no-one was looking. This in our view demonstrated such a naïve and childishly blinkered view of the way games are played at the top level in real life as to place them outside the pale. Anyway, Haig Street was in another ward, and they went to another school, where they had to wear caps, so what else could you expect?

The two groups had problems common to both, and at odd moments when bat or ball were not to hand, and we had nothing better to do, such as chasing Elsie Dangerfield (she was very quick on her feet in those pre-pubertal days, and was rated good sport; later she slowed down for one reason or another, and got a reputation for being an even better sport), we would engage in desultory discussion on such tricky questions as whether the flick of the ball on a flapping trouser-leg was sufficient, or did it need to thud on solid flesh? Willie McTaggart was our Party Theorist, a hard man in such matters who kept us on the strict dogmatic line. I met him again the other day in Whitehall; he had just been chairing an *ad hoc* inter-departmental sub-committee of senior civil servants preparing the fourth draft of a preliminary working-paper which may lead to a report which might be submitted to the Cabinet Office Think Tank (Treasury Sub-Division), on whether cricketers' boxes should be classed, for taxation purposes, as protective or cosmetic. He considers that the only significant difference between the arguments he is engaged in now and was then is that around Kitchener Street the standard of English was marginally higher.

But this story is about human personality, and the depths of degradation to which it can sink. It is specifically about the aforementioned Bobby Gorbelly, and the pernicious part French Cricket played in his Fall.

There are those who say that the French had nothing to do with this perversion of our national game, but I suspect that a particular adjective doesn't get linked with an exclusive noun of such importance without good reason.

Take French kissing, for example: what could be more Gallic? And a perversion if ever there was. Like many another British lad, I lived under its evil influence from the day my hormones started to stir, and I can tell you that is a heavy load to shoulder at the age of 35. I firmly intend to give it up the moment I find out just what it is. An older friend, worldly-wise, once told me to switch to fluoride, but I didn't understand, and I suspect he was teasing me. It happens.

What about French leave? The French horn? French cooking? French windows? The French Revolution?

In all these is demonstrated the one factor which has denied France the true greatness which we assume is ours by right, but which is, in fact, nothing of the sort. Our pre-eminence is earned by a dogged application of irresistible inertia, as epitomized by our transport system, and taking five days over failing to get a result in a Test match.

The French Factor, if I may so call it, is overindulgence. Take the list above: each has a sound British equivalent which our Continental neighbours, incontinent, distort by taking too far. Thus, in this country, leave is being absent without anyone noticing; a horn is something you toot occasionally, and on one note only; cooking is preparing food with minimal enthusiasm and no seasoning; a window is for light to go through, not people; and a revolution involves turning things around until everyone is back in exactly the same relative position as when it started. That perversity is not too strong a word is substantiated by the French combination of ardour in sex with garlic in everything.

Bobby was of mixed race. He was quite bold-faced about it, and for that we admired him. He claimed to be one-third English, and although a later smattering of Biology led me to question the ratio,

[23]

there was no doubt his Mum talked funny, and he used to Go South on holiday sometimes – well beyond Galashiels, some said.

After one such trip he came back, Prometheus-like, bearing knowledge which first revolutionized our local games, and then ruined them. It may be that time, the great healer, has by now restored the *status quo ante*, but for our generation Bobby's selfishly crazy act destroyed a whole way of play, and probably sowed seeds that later flowered as the evil weeds of wife-battering and divorce.

We knew, of course, that you could be out if caught straight from the bat, but the rule was seldom brought into play – mainly we went for bold frontal shin-crushing, with the occasional caught-and-bowled as a freakish extra.

Bobby discovered on his travels (where, he would never tell us, being bound by dreadful oaths) that if you hurl the ball hard so that it bounces just in front of the bat, it is practically impossible for the batsman to prevent it rebounding upwards, giving an easy catch. There is a countering technique; I learnt it much later from the *maître d'hôtel* of the Negresco in Nice – we met at the Scarborough festival – but I also am tied by my word, and cannot reveal it here.

On the very evening of his return home, Bobby brought his team round to challenge us. We were routed. We didn't know what had hit us, or rather, hadn't. Each of us got out first ball with never a bruise to show for it. It was humiliating. To be slaughtered in battle was bad enough, but to be without a single wound to advertise our suffering was intolerable.

Next day we played again. Once again we were soundly beaten, but this time we watched what was being done to us, and we learnt. It is for just such traumatic crises that Nature has provided Man with a rapidly re-programmable cerebral cortex. Soon we had analysed and perfected the technique, and began using it against our tormentors. Quite soon we were once more on an even footing – particularly in home matches, when our rules applied.

Of course, the game was changed, irrevocably; a discontinuous shift in our cricket evolution had occurred which could never be reversed. Nonetheless, the new game was exciting, and we were happy. Particularly invigorating was applying the new method to the wets of Haig Street. We were like a troupe of Torquemadas with the latest thing in thumb-screws. We trounced them; we thrashed them; we thumped them; we spiflicated them. I remember that period vividly as a succession of bright sunny days; life was good, and what was more, it could have gone on indefinitely. They never came near to sorting out what was happening to them, spending so much time asserting vociferously that in a perfect world such things would not occur that they never got round to working out why it was occurring, and thence moving on to do something about it. We had established a perfect slave-master relationship, than which there is nothing more pleasant, if you happen to be the master.

Bobby blew it.

We should have seen it coming, but we had no experience in these matters. We should have noticed that Doris Dangerfield, Elsie's elder sister, had begun to slow down, especially when Bobby was around. It should have been obvious, for his shape forced her matching deceleration to be as near infinite as makes little difference.

It's an old story: Bobby was poor, his Dad drove a No. 23 bus. Doris's Daddy was a master butcher, thus raising her a cut above the rest of us. Bobby had nothing material to give her to prove his devotion, so he gave what he had.

He told her.

A girl.

He might as well have taken a page in *The Beano*.

Within fifteen minutes all Haig Street was in the picture.

That was the end of it; by next day they had practised the trick until they were thoroughly familiar with it. When next we played them, we merely won heavily, and all the fun had gone for any bunch of idiots could have beaten that lot.

You will be pleased to hear, this being a moral tale, that retribution caught up with Bobby Gorbelly in the end. Doris kept her hooks in him, and at seventeen they ran away to Gretna Green. Daddy cut her off with a shilling, but forgot to formalize his wishes on paper, so when he walked under Bobby's Dad's bus, Doris picked up a tidy sum.

They emigrated to West Africa, where Bobby built up a chain

of night-clubs of low repute and high profitability. He is now very rich, has a bundle tied up in untouchable pension rights, and has trained up a group of competent managers so that all he has to do is jet around the world's capitals auditioning dancing-girls for his cabaret-spots. My wife says that is no life for a man, and a lesson to us all.

I met him not long ago in town. He looked tired.

Beach Cricket

I HAVE a Rhodes Scholar American friend who claims, with some justice, that two major pieces of evidence for the irremediable idiocy of the English are, first, that they should in this climate have invented a game utterly dependent on the absence of rain over a continuous period of more than seven hours, and second, that in the face of over two hundred years of watery evidence they should still be playing it.

Since he is the same friend who claims that the possession of sunglasses in this country is the height of vulgar ostentation, we must take his comments with some degree of caution. Cricket addicts may be further inclined to dismiss each and all of his opinions on every topic from sport right down to the world economic situation as the product of a twisted mind when I report his comment on a day at Lord's: he said it had 'all the inherent excitement of watching paint dry'. The blanket rejection of his views over the range quoted may thicken in texture when I reveal that he is, nowadays, a highly respected member of the United States Treasury.

It is not, of course, his fault. He was brought up in a society that holds sport and business at their best when the former most closely resembles the latter, and neither is in any way influenced by the peculiarities of people or the waywardness of weather; whose idea of a perfect sporting occasion is a Double-Header crammed into a single evening, on artificial turf, in artificial light, under a plastic sky, at controlled temperature and humidity, accompanied by the consumption of mongrel hot-dogs and caffeine-laced synthetically flavoured carbonated recycled water, the whole ending in a fixed result.

Some of the greatest matches I have ever known have been those in which climatic chance has evoked individual idiosyncrasy to swing success from the settled sway of one side to the amazed authority of the other. One thinks of brilliant off-spin after rain-seepage; tight seaming under errant cloud; emergent aggression on a drying sticky. But the interplay I remember best was that between a large jelly-fish and a little tender compassion; the former completely altered the complexions of a sole and a potential humiliation, while the second settled the life-styles of two people in a pattern wildly the reverse of their expectations, and incidentally ruined my lunch yesterday.

Let me explain . . .

In my early teens, I played cricket on the beach every afternoon throughout the whole month of July. Yes, every single one without fail, for in those days the sun blazed brightly from the marvellous moment on 1st July, when my father awarded me a shining new shilling for being the first to catch sight of the sea as we breasted the crest before the coast – I always won it, for that day was my birthday. It shone until the sad second on the 31st when my brother won – it was his birthday – for being the last to see it sparkle as we gazed back through the rear window.

In the mornings we chased happiness among the dunes, and caught it frequently, sliding down the sand slopes in hectic sequence, leaping the high cliffs to soft landings with billowing beach-towel parachutes, Beau Gesting to a rival group's Riffs with dash, courage, and the smell of hot baker's pies for lunch wafting back from the beach huts to tell us the Legion would get there on time.

In the evenings some of us crept more quietly among the same dunes, observing our older brothers and sisters chasing their happiness in what seemed to us a more inhibited and uncomfortable way, although the number of wedding invitations that appeared on our parents' mantelpieces each following January would have forced us to revise the 'inhibited' had we yet reached the stage of comprehending the 'uncomfortable'.

But in the afternoons – ah! those transcendent, sun-soaked, beach-pond-paddling afternoons, that lasted from early lunch till always – stumps were pitched as soon as a quorum of them could be collected, and a game broke out. The phrase is deliberate, for much of the time they were amorphous affairs, each against all, with a floating population of fielders waiting their turn with bat or ball. No-one really knew the rules, and certainly we were unaware that they were Laws.

Sometimes a pompous parent claimed control, adulterating our pure pleasure with his serious intent, but most of the time the play drifted on as play should, spontaneous and with no obvious direction either from above or in view. It used to puzzle me then, and it puzzles me again now that the burden of my own parental responsibilities has stopped squashing my brain into an absurd shape, why grown-ups cannot accept as an adequate, even exhaustive, answer to the question 'What have you been doing?' the simple reply, 'Playing.'

When a game is a true game such as ours, conditions do not matter. In fact, as long as they permit play their problems add spice, and are incorporated without wrangle or rancour into the *de facto* rules. Children accept readily that rules must reflect reality, and never try to obscure the obvious to save the theorem. If the sand is so soft that a pitching ball stops dead, then a local regulation emerges permitting the keeper to take it before the stumps. If Billie Arnstruther's young brothers have buried their father up to his neck in the sand at square leg, then the umpire stands at cover point, and if the tide is in and cover point is three feet under, he stands up by the ice-cream kiosk. Umpires don't really matter anyway, since they are usually weedy cousins voted into the office to keep them out of the game while satisfying parental insistence that they be included in the group. In any case, most decisions are by general acclamation.

Sometimes, however, more organized matches took place, between fairly fixed teams, such as Locals versus Visitors, Beach-hutters opposing Wind-breakers, or South Pier against West Groin. (Familiar with these last structures from early holidays I was puzzled at my first Test match when, a rearing good-length ball having laid the batsman low, I heard the gentleman behind me explain to his lady that the blow had been on such a one; I could understand the hollow thud I had heard, but I couldn't see why he should have a structure of that sort just there, or why his face had turned green.)

On such occasions, conditions became more relevant, but not in any negative way. No light-meters for us, no fussing over a small ridge at the Nursery end. Covering the wicket was pointless – Canute had tried. Environmental variables were noted and where possible exploited. For example, we used to perform on a pretty flat stretch of firm sand which played true under most conditions, but with certain combinations of tide, wind and current the receding waters left it corrugated in fine ripples. If these were at right-angles to the shore – for some reason, never questioned, beach pitches are always tangential to the prom-enade, no matter what the compass bearing – the result was an exercise in variable lift, and was the same for both sides. If, however, they ran at an angle, the case was altered; our team won many a match because Billie Arnstruther's Dad went fishing (when he wasn't buried up to his neck in the sand) with a man who knew someone who could predict which way they would run. Billie said his Dad said it was a matter of asking a local to have another pint the night before, and watching which way his Adam's apple wobbled when he said 'Aaaarrrgh'.

Personally I rather doubted this, though I had to admit that Billie's Dad was remarkably reliable on such matters, and I reckoned that if you could do it, you must know how it was done. I had not at that time studied in depth the evolution of the British political system. Knowing the ridge-angle in advance, we would simply pack our side with off- or leg-spinners as the situation demanded, and it was in the bag. Billie's Dad explained the only time he got it wrong as a side-effect of an epidemic of acute laryngitis.

To explain the significance of the match I mentioned earlier, I have to make a point which may seem anti-feminist, but is not so intended. Children have no views on feminism; they do not know it exists, so cannot consciously oppose or support it. Of course, their upbringing may have built into them attitudes which they do not realize are imposed rather than inherent, but I am not arguing about what might or ought to be; I am remembering what was, or was thought to be.

When I was that age, it was generally accepted by my contemporaries of both sexes that on the whole, taking a broad view, the thick with the thin, smoothing out the bumps, girls were a dead loss as far as games were concerned. In fact, up to the age of about fifteen, the overwhelming opinion among the boys was that girls were a dead loss in every way. Later on, when the bumps could no longer be smoothed out, we adopted a different sort of broad view, realized the advantage of going for the thick rather than the thin, and headed back to the dunes. But my memory of that phase is, perhaps mercifully, meagre. As Billie Arnstruther himself recently summed it up, it is easy to recall how we used to chase girls, but it is difficult to remember quite why.

It is nonetheless a fact that to us, then, the notion of a competent female cricketer was a contradiction in terms, and the idea of a good one an absurdity. Girls held bats with hands reversed, they bowled as if their arms were on the wrong sides, and they couldn't catch a cold so were only useful as fielders if you packed them solid and let the ball bounce off them; even in that role they could not be relied upon to stand still long enough to maintain a credible defence.

Then into our lives burst the Lusty girls, shattering for one brief span our comfortable sexual certainty. They arrived on the scene suddenly, in mid-month, a ready-made family of four formidable females led by a monumental mother. There must have been a father about somewhere, I suppose, but that woman was so potent she probably preferred parthenogenesis. No-one

[31]

knew where they had come from; looking back I suspect somewhere on the east side of South America. They were certainly amazonian in their aptitude to things physical; the best word to describe their looks is handsome, and in their attitude to life they matched their name.

They looked like triplets, but were a single and twins with a bare year between. Their names were really Amanda, Jemima and Josephine, but they always called themselves Man, Jem and Jo, and were so known to us. They could out-run, out-jump, out-throw all of us, and they could shout louder. They could swim faster and further, dive deeper, build better sand-castles, and Jem could even spit further than Gobby McAllister, who was reputed to have brought down a wasp in flight from clear across the prom.

It was humiliating, and worse was to come, for quite soon they established that they could bat, bowl, catch, and field as well as if not better than any of us. It had to be admitted that they were an asset to our routine games, and we accepted them into those without much hesitation, but (and here I see the genesis of adult techniques of discrimination) we made sure the doubt implied in the 'if not better' was never resolved by refusing to pick them for proper matches.

After two of these shut-outs, Mother Lusty stepped in, and she was one of those people who, when they take action, make it jangle. She combed the entire length of the beach (this in itself verging on treason), talent-spotting, bribing, cajoling, and (what she did best) domineering, until she came up with an all-girl team of considerable talent.

When they challenged us we tried to ignore them, but adult opinion was against us for two reasons. Partly it was because this was just after the war, when there still remained a residue of the feeling of equality engendered by the need for 'mucking in together' imposed by the National Emergency. On the other hand, it may just have been something to do with the way our dads buzzed round Mrs Lusty like bees round a honeypot when she appeared in one of the new and extremely daring 'bikinis'.

The match was set for the penultimate day of the holiday. The girls won the argument over who was to bat first (they could do that better, too, but that was natural), and the twins opened; at half-past three they were still there with the score on 183. Degradation deepened for we simply could not budge them, and at tea-time they were 167 and 168 not out respectively, but since they were identical nobody knew in what respect.

In beach cricket, declaration does not normally apply since a result is seldom sought, but in this case the girls wanted their pound of flesh, and it was agreed that the game should be carried over to the next morning, while the mums cleared out the beach huts in preparation for our collective dispersal as we went our various ways for another year. The girls set their field, our openers took their places, and Man Lusty began her run-up to the wicket.

Man bowled a mean in-swinger, and there is little doubt in my mind now that she would have winkled us out in no time at all, though none of us would have admitted it then, but that was the moment when the elements swayed events. The tide had, of course, advanced and ebbed overnight, and had deposited a massive sand-coated jelly-fish just to one side of the bowling-crease. For some reason – the unusual tension I suppose – no-one noticed it, not even Man, and as she ran in to deliver the first ball she slapped her bare foot hard down on the tentacles which were trailing over the line. The animal was freshly deposited, still alive, and it stung her quite severely.

Thus the match ended, in tears and screams on one side, moderate concern and huge relief on the other. Who knows, we said, we probably would have knocked them off with ease. In following years, the dimming of memory permitted probability to usurp certainty, and mini-masculine honour was salved.

But what, you say, of the two lives changed, and the lunch ruined? It was this way. Billie Arnstruther was our captain and that rarity, a beautiful boy: not in any namby-pamby way, for he was strong and powerfully athletic, but he was of the sort that die early in a war, and are remembered as the flower of their nation. He was also full of great personal compassion, and when Amanda was hurt, he was the first at her side. Theseus-like, he carried her, not to his ship, but to the first-aid tent, where he stayed by her side and gave her comfort and his iced lolly to suck.

All very romantic? Yes it was, for when the Lustys moved on to fresh resorts in the following years, the Arnstruthers followed, and as Man and Billie grew in years, so they grew in love, and in the fulness of time they married.

I knew nothing of these developments until just recently, when I found Arnstruther-Lusty iii sitting at a desk in front of me. He is a horror of the first quality, a spineless, featureless brat of no discernible intelligence, characterized only by lack of organization, and it was an attempt to read his first piece of homework that spoiled my lunch yesterday.

I have never met the older offspring, but they tell me that the first is a handsome lad who reminds everyone of Amanda, while the second is an entrancing lass who reminds everyone of Billie; this is a neat but not unusual example of Sex-linked Inheritance Crossing-over.

The third is obviously another kettle of marine life entirely. I wonder if *Nature* would be interested in a paper on 'Sole Mediation in Inter-Specific Gene Transfer'?

Number Three reminds me strongly of the jelly-fish.

Street Cricket

IT WAS HIM OR ME.

The steel in his eye spelt lead in my belly if I made a false move.

The Dust stirred in the dry yard; a child whimpered; time stood still, and my hair on end.

He went for his silver six-guns, numerously notched; he was fast, faster than anyone around these parts except one – me.

Before the tip of his foresight was clear of the leather, mine was lined up on his shabby sheriff's star.

I stitched sixteen shots across his shirt, lusting in my speed and power.

He had to give me best this time; leaping on his trusty white steed he rode hell-for-leather out of the compound, straight on to Main Street, where he was nearly run down by a van delivering crisps to Granny McGie's sweet shop on the corner.

But it wasn't just this time: it was every time, and not only with me. Harry Hill always lost his fights. He was a dear, sweet boy, truly nice when nice still had some meaning, gay before the word was perverted, and peaceable while it did not require aggressive demonstration. He only got to be sheriff because the cinema was going through one of its creatively original anti-hero phases again, when the cowboys on the white horses turn out to be the mean *hombres*, the noble injuns whup the cowardly cavalry, and the wicked homesteaders maliciously destroy fine cattle grazing with their shorthorn sheep and unbrandable buckwheat.

Harry was ten, sole boy and youngest of a family of seven, and growing up under the high-heels of such a monstrous regiment he had quickly learnt that, since argument is pointless if advantage is unattainable, and trying to win word wars against females is folly, it made for a more comfortable life gratefully to accept whatever they told him he wanted. He has made his later life extremely comfortable by reversing the principle; he has for years written the health and beauty column in a national weekly, telling his readers what they want to hear, and advising them to do whatever they feel like doing. He is a confirmed bachelor.

In the morning he may have lost a confrontation at the OK Corral, but in the afternoon he was the captain of our cricket side. Captain is not the word we used, for we knew nothing of the office, of tossing coins and setting fields, of switching the order and bringing on the spinners. Truth to tell, we knew very little about cricket at all; those were the days before television. *Test Match Special* did not penetrate into our tenements, and few of us had ever seen a field wide enough to hold a herd of cows, never mind a deep extra cover. We played an anarchic version of the game, based on hearsay and back copies of *The Champion*.

As an example, take our lbw rule. We reckoned that if, as the bowler ran up to the wicket, he could not see all three stumps full clear, due to the intermediation of any part of the batsman's person, it constituted a *prima facie* case of 'out'. We had no umpires – the very notion of umpire was alien to our ethos – and such cases were flung before a committee of the whole House. This was not quite so chaotic as it sounds, or as inconclusive as the metaphor implies, for it usually meant that if Billy Whingy thought you were out, and we all shouted agreement, and Harry nodded assent, that was it: you walked. Harry had to give his assent, for it was 'his game'; we had to voice agreement, for it was a democratic society; but Billy was our accepted Leader, for he was bigger by a head than any of us, and vicious when roused, so the assent and the agreement were assured by a discipline with more physical reality than a printed whip. The rule may seem odd, but it had the merit of simplicity compared with the present random reality. I am forced at times to think that the only charitable way to explain some of the decisions given nowadays is that the umpires are applying a similar interpretation, and are thus unconsciously reverting to their first childhood rather than incoherently slipping into their second.

We had no equipment. The bat was a section from a fruit-box, our stumps were chalked on Ron Flannery's front door (his Mum spent all day round at the wash-house, and his Old Man was on nights and slept through the day in the back room). Many of the teams we played had no ball, but you can get a lot of noise and movement off the pitch with an empty corned-beef tin. We had a ball, real leather; looking back I seem to remember the seam snaking sigmoidally round the surface, so I suspect it was a soft-ball left behind by the Yanks billeted in the Catholic school during the war. Nonetheless, it gave us considerable status, and we were invited to play matches in quite a few of the most exclusive local no-go areas. This was not a description we used in those days, but it fits. I grew up on the edge of a vast slum that stretched deep into the heart of the city. Administratively we were just outside the city boundary but socially we were part of it, and the society was tribal, the demarcations doctrinal. We could not for any other reason have ventured with impunity into another group's patch, but cricket and our real leather ball took us safely in.

Only one other playing area that I knew was, like ours, in a street. Streets are busy places: traffic trundles, women gossip, washing waves, doorsteps gleam. If you touched either the third or fourth of these, you were attacked by the second, and in fleeing might fall under the first.

Two of our neighbours played on partially cleared bomb sites, which were sheltered but favoured the home side, who knew where the craters were. One lot had taken over the flat roof on the top of our only semi-skyscraper, a twenty-storey office block, empty and derelict. Its major defect was that a lofted pull meant not only six and out, but also a fifteen minute break in the game – the lifts didn't work.

Another group pitched their stumps (two packing cases) in the abandoned shell of the communal open-air swimming pool donated by an emigrant who had made his fortune in his new Californian home and had forgotten the climate of his old Scottish one. Fielding in it was easy – the ball bounced back off the walls like the puck in an ice-rink – but batting was tricky and polar, for a good length ball at one end whizzed past your ankles horizontally, one inch off the ground, while the same ball at the other hit you straight on the crown of the head almost directly from above.

We played in a street; it was, effectively, a cul-de-sac, at least in the holidays, for at the far end was the main entrance of the local primary school. We kept well away from that end; we spent an awful chunk of our lives inside those gates, and we didn't want to risk additional accidental incarceration. Education at that level was an efficient but brutal business. When I got to my public school at the age of twelve I was fully two years ahead of my prep-school educated fellows, but it took two more years before I was able to relax inside a classroom and begin to enjoy learning. Soon after I arrived, my English master commented in my hearing that I had obviously been given a good grounding in grammar; at the time it had felt more like a grinding. We were beaten into shape; an apt phrase, for it was a rare day that we escaped a dose of the tawse, that heavy leather strap applied with vigour to the outstretched trembling hand. When we children were taken *en masse* to watch the terrible news-films of the liberation of the Nazi concentration camps, we sat in silence, mercifully unable to comprehend or relate to what was going on until right at the end, when they showed the guards being rounded up. This we recognized as the day-dream whose fulfilment we longed for passionately between nine o'clock and four every week-day most of the year, and to the horror of the accompanying adults we burst into shouts of 'There's Beany! That's old Baggy Bloomers!'

'Look, they've nabbed the headmaster! Shifty, in't 'e?'

'Hangin's too good for 'em; give 'em six double-handers!'

The Scottish education system was always said to give its pupils a great respect for learning; that may have been so – we certainly had a healthy respect for that school and kept well away from it whenever possible.

Another reason for keeping our distance from those gates was that any ball hit over them was lost forever. Just inside, in a sort of lodge, lived the headmaster, although we never thought of him as living, rather as lurking. Living was what humans did, and we did not allow teachers classification in that species. We reckoned God made us and our Mums and Dads, and even Billy Whingy and PC Boot, on the Saturday; on the Sunday He woke up to the realization that He had forgotten teachers, so they got made when He was tired after a hard week and in a bad temper because it was supposed to be His day off.

There was plenty of space inside the school grounds. It would have been ideal for cricket or roller-skating, or any sort of holiday play, but we were rigidly excluded except during school hours. Nobody thought then of using schools for any sort of community activity: there were no PTAs, no Badminton Club in the Hall, no Drama Group on the stage. It may have been an educational oasis, but it was a cultural desert. Recently I played cricket on the beach with some boys of about the age I was then; they were from 'deprived' backgrounds in a different, more southern city. They told me they could never play cricket back home, and when I asked why they didn't use their school yard, they answered pityingly, 'The 'ookers tikes it hover arter school's aht, don't they?'

I suppose this is an advance on our situation – at least the space has been allocated for some sort of recreational purpose, but the professionalism distresses me.

There was a fine municipal park – Jubilee Park – just down the road from us, but its policy was a total negation of its name. Far from emancipation, stark notices and stern keepers patrolled the verges to limit incursion to the paths. Tempting stretches of lush grass never bore anything heavier than a mower and the longing glances of Sunday-walking, best-suited (only-suited) boys. As for trumpets, there was a grand bandstand, beautifully kept and well appointed, but in all my years in the locality, on only two occasions did a band actually play in it, and that in an area laden down with Company brass. Perhaps the fundamentalist leanings of our elders had touched the interpretation of the name, and the fiftieth anniversary just did not happen to fall within my short fifteen years of experience. On the other hand, it may be that the theory I heard proposed recently is true, that the major qualification for becoming a City Father is cerebral sterility.

Most of one side of our street was occupied by a transport garage, which was not so hazardous to street cricketers as it sounds, for nearly all the lorries moved out early in the morning and returned late in the day. In any case, the street ran straight down a steep hill, so we could hear them coming as they revved up and changed gear to turn into it from the main road at the bottom. The slope also meant that you had to pack the field on that side to stop the gentlest tap scoring 28 while a fielder waited for a break in the traffic to fetch the ball. Luckily there was no point in having many fielders on the other side – that way lay the school, and no batsman dared hit the ball hard in that direction.

As I have said, we used to chalk our stumps on Mrs Flannery's front door, and this brings me on to some technical points about illustrations of Street Cricket. They nearly all show the batsman defending a wicket painted boldly on a wall, or the base of a lamp-post. My experience, recalled but dimly I must admit, insists on three errors in such scenes:

1. No child would paint stumps boldly – he wouldn't have access to paint, and he wouldn't have dared to deface municipal property if he had. We could usually nick the odd piece of chalk (even the concentration camp inmates managed to steal some necessities from their tormentors), and chalk could be rapidly rubbed away if heavy leather was heard in the land.
2. In our streets, all the walls had pavements in front of them; if you bat facing out from a wall, a good length ball hits the kerb and either bounces straight back at the bowler, or rears vertically and lands on the batsman's head. We were in a special circumstance, for the manoeuvring mammoths had flattened

our kerbs until they merged into the tarmac of the road.

3. Our lamp-posts were all corrugated horizontally, and it was impossible to draw straight lines down them. In any case, there was always a grating in the gutter just in front of a lamp-post, which was awkward to stand on, and the bottle screw-tops we bowled with if Harry wasn't about tended to disappear down the holes when you smothered a yorker.

We didn't play cricket all the time; actually we didn't play it much of the time. Our two main occupations were football and fighting. We saw them as different sports, keeping them strictly apart. Judging by what I see on the television these days, they have now merged, on and off the field. That is a pity, for the rules were slightly different, the major modification being that no impedimenta of any sort were permitted in soccer; no-one would even have thought of bringing stick, stone, bottle, or airgun to a properly convened ball game, not even as a spectator. It simply wasn't done; we had our standards.

But it is the cricket that I remember most clearly. Football and feuding, cowboys and indians, wall-walking and Peever (how could a Scot call it Hopscotch?), these were all background activities, and have sunk into that miasmic middle distance which makes up most of memory. It was also its loss I felt most bitterly when all our street play was destroyed in the twin upheavals of the Brave New Post-war World. Twin they were in effect, though not in scale. The major change involved the Great Ones of the City Corporation, and swept away the street play of our fellows over the urban boundary. The minor one was the sole responsibility of PC Boot, and did the same for us.

The latter first, for it takes little telling. PC Boot simply enforced the letter of the law. Until he arrived, our local bobby had been a member of the community; he supped a pint in the local at lunchtime, and a cuppa in Mrs Hill's front room around halfpast three. It was said he was particularly partial to potato scones, Mrs Hill's speciality, and his waistline amplified this hypothesis, though we sometimes wondered how he could spend a full hour eating scones. He used to chide us gently for 'Hobstruction hov the King's 'ighway' (he was foreign, maybe even

English), but we paid little attention, for neither His Majesty nor Dick Turpin came along our street all that often – we would at that age have cheered either with equal fervour, but later some of the lads went a bit political and would have rallied to the latter more readily than the former.

Then our fat flat-footed friend retired, or was retired, and was replaced by what was grandly described as a 'Flying Patrol', but looked like a bored copper in a car. This was Police Constable Boot, ex-MI4½, ambitious, the peak of his cap resting on the bridge of his nose, beady eyes questing for crime. There wasn't much of it about in our street, so he created it by chasing us off our natural playing- and hunting-grounds. When we kept on coming back, he arrested Billy Whingy, and pushed through a prosecution. He got a conviction – and his way, for our mothers, fearful, fulfilled his fiat and kept us off the streets. He also launched Billy on a career that has cost Their Successive Majesties enormous sums in boarding fees.

The major catastrophe was the slum clearance programme initiated by well-meaning politicians with naïve notions of how to achieve Utopia, and implemented by blinkered boffins and rhetorical architects. This was the heyday of the High-Rise Flat, monstrous buildings pointing obscenely heavenwards, in which the higher you were placed the closer you came to hell. It is now accepted that they were social disasters on a huge scale; luckily few will last long enough to become memorials, for their detail was as crudely constructed as their concept, and those that have not had to be blown up are rapidly falling down.

In this essay I am concerned merely with their effect on street cricket, and they destroyed it utterly. The tawdry tenements were razed, and modish monuments to money-making raised in their place. The bomb-sites and the old pool were cleared, metalled, and marked as car-parks for the clerks who never came to the instantly redundant offices. Cricket in the area died; all games, play, fun died; the very area died. The tribes were broken up and dispersed into aching anonymity. Play areas were planned into the spaces between the towers but they were never used, for how can a caring mother maintain her apron-strings unsnapped from twenty storeys up when the lift has been vandalized? In any case, who can play any sort of worthwhile cricket in the permanent gales induced by the physics of such prodigious piles?

What happened to all those characters? I went away to school and lost touch; Billy and Harry moved into the spheres I have mentioned, both, I am happy to say, well outside my own experience. The planners and the architects got knighthoods, riches, and a chance to do better next time; a few of them have. The City got a crime wave which surprised it enormously, and surprise has rigged its response ever since. PC Boot got his promotion and his come-uppance at the same stroke: he was transferred into sole charge of a sub-station slap in the centre of the new flats.

One puzzle may remain in your minds. Why was Harry Hill captain of our side? Why did we have to seek his approval for every move we made in our matches? There is a nice analogy here (nice in the strict sense) with the present position of the United States in the Western Alliance, and if we follow it along it may be illuminating. Harry was a hopeless games-player; he was big and strong and likeable, but not very quick, and if he tried to think and move at the same time, he tripped over his own big feet, often landing on someone else's. He was poorly coordinated, badly trained, naïve about the hard realities of gamesmanship, but his main problem, and that of those who played with him, was his inability to grasp the real point of the exercise.

In baseball, the captain is said the 'call the shots'. In the present world situation this may have unfortunate military overtones, but the Americans are able to do it for exactly the same reason as Harry.

He owned the ball.

Legal Cricket

RELIGIOUS BELIEF, they say, is the celestial subjugation of fact by faith. Moderates may dismiss such a statement as verging on the cynical, but I find it reveals the mentalities of both sides, for it is the sort of sentence that the Faithful dissect fanatically at prayer-meetings, and end up by accepting joyfully as an inspired but realistic assessment of their position; convinced atheists, on the other hand, analyse it in depth in secular study-groups, and by consensus acclaim it soberly as a powerful but valid justification of their stance.

If you squeeze a believer, the juice of personal experience runs out. If you chip away the soft-wood props of loose logic and doubtful evidence with which time and careless custom have cluttered their positions, the true believers are left standing, rock-solid, on a sound support of personal revelation. Ultimately, they know because they know; they are happy to accept a shaky general edifice because their particularity is pier and proofing enough for all. It is a standing which is unshakable from without.

From my own wobbling instability as one who is agnostic about his agnosticism, it is enviable.

I mention all this because it is the precise reverse of my beliefs about the Law of the Land. I am happy to accept the majesty of the whole system because as a whole it seems to work better than any other, but only so long as I exclude rigidly from my consideration my own personal brushes with the dusty hem of its regal robes. And I mention it here because each of my brushes has bristled with points of cricketing interest. Let me relate . . .

In my childhood I had two Uncle Bobs; the first was one of those pseudo-uncles who plague one's youth and embarrass one's adulthood. They tend to be parental associates who have to be entertained; true family friends do not need their acceptance justified by titles. This Uncle Bob was the family lawyer; at least, he had handled my grandfather's estate, and we had inherited him with it. It didn't come to much, but then neither did he. My father had little use for lawyers, in either sense, and would have been mad to employ Uncle Bob if he had, for he was not only absolutely amoral, but totally incompetent. The two attributes seemed to cancel each other out in his legal practice, and he made a good living on the side as an absentee slum landlord. Uncle Bob gave me my first taste of Lawyer; it was tainted and lasting.

It took a few years after my grandfather's death before my parents could extricate themselves socially from this monster, and in that period my poor Dad got sucked into a local professional group, mainly legal, whose idea of a fun weekend was to cart their families off to a certain popular holiday resort, decant them into the Hotel Splendide to amuse themselves, and pass their own days at the racecourse and their evenings at the bar. As a family, we got trapped into two of these trips. They were abject misery for us all but they taught me a valuable lesson, for I discovered that vulgarity has a really unpleasant implication only at the upper end of the social, or rather, financial scale. I was able to compare, in the course of each day, the behaviour of the people on beach and promenade with that of those in the grand hotel. The former was vulgar in the original sense, jostling, noisy, smelly, flashy, tawdry, and, in the evenings, a little intemperate, but rich in honest enjoyment and open fun. Everything in the hotel was enormously expensive and supposedly of the best, but with the clarity of a child's vision I saw through the imperial pretension to the blotchy nakedness beneath, and noted that it also was jostling, noisy, smelly, flashy, tawdry, and, in the evenings, boozed up to the gills. The difference was that, underneath the forced gaiety, the mad hectic whirl, nobody was actually enjoying themselves; they all seemed the sort of people whose presence destroys solitude without creating companionship.

Then we discovered the cricket festival. The ground in Weltown is not easy to find, for it can be described geographically as an area of grass completely surrounded by landladies. The streets which skirt it modestly mask its very existence in an urban purdah, so that only its intimates ever taste its attractions. The houses behind whose backs it lies buried might be described as mean, but only by those whose notion of generosity is limited. We found it by accident, but for many years thereafter we made our annual pilgrimage and took our fill of runs, wickets, the shared cheerfulness of satisfied spectatorship, and the potent pancakes of Mrs Tewksbury of the Seaview Private Hotel (Beach and Shopping Centre within Easy Walking Distance). I have very happy memories of that ground and of the quality of the sport it provided. It was my introduction to cricket at high level, and it was many years before I realized that it is not always played in the same joyful and adventurous spirit. I suppose I owe the introduction to Bad Uncle Bob, and I can hardly lay on him the later inevitable disillusionment when I saw the game put to the Test.

Good Uncle Bob was real; that is, he was a real uncle, my mother's brother. We did not see very much of him in terms of frequency, for he lived in the Far South, Wales or somewhere Very Distant like that, but when he was with us we saw a lot of him for he was a huge man, six feet long in all directions. When I was little, and stood near him. I could not see his head when I looked up at him; my father told me much later that he reckoned from the age of fifteen onwards Bob had been unable to determine merely by looking down whether he was still male. I capped his surprisingly *risqué* remark with one of my own, to the effect that I did not see how any self-respecting female would have allowed him to find out in any other way, and that perhaps it was the uncertainty that led him to pontificate so dogmatically on every subject under the sun. My father, stout Presbyter that he was, stated himself unable to understand why a pontiff, of all people, should have to assert his masculinity in any case, and the discussion drowned with decent deliberation in the lower levels of sectarian slander. Uncle Bob seemed to think that every event, even on the fringes of his attention, required from him an instant definitive statement, and he spent most of his time delivering them. Since this gave him little or no chance to find out what anything was about at all his assertive clarifications were usually hilariously misinformed. But it was a waste of time pointing out an error for he refused to lose any contest, and would simply and blatantly switch his argument, if necessary completely into reverse. The time-wasting could be amusing, however, and it became a family game to see how often you could get Uncle Bob to change his unswerving direction in a discussion. He always won, by force of his overbearing avoir-dupois, and in our household to this day an attempt to win a debate by force of arms rather than argument is called 'a piece of daylight Bobbery'.

Uncle Bob hardly ever played games, and nobody ever played games with him more than once if they could avoid it. To be absolutely correct, I should say more than nearly once, for he was a poor player, always rapidly rushing towards defeat, always refusing to accept that defeat, and always petulantly plunging away from the game to avoid the inevitable end of the 'silly nonsense'. Only once did I know him try to force a contest to conclusion in the heat of hazard, and that cost him dear.

We had gone to visit him at long last, for the first and only time, as a detour tacked on to the end of an extensive foreign trip that had taken us as far afield as Colwyn Bay. We changed trains at Crewe on the way down. It turned out that Uncle Bob lived near Chester, which seemed to us as nearly in Wales as didn't make much difference, though he appeared to think it did, and told us how in a wealth of detail and language which I am glad to say I did not understand, and quickly forgot. When we reached Crewe on the way back, we broke our journey and stayed with him over an eventful weekend.

[47]

Three things are burned deep into my memory from that weekend; the food, the Court, and the Car Cricket. As to the first, my uncle maintained his bulk on a steady stream of sugar in sundry guises, and to our parents' horror and our delight we children lived for two glorious days on an endless supply of sweets and chocolate and cream-cakes and ice-cream and trifle and jammy-dodgers and sherbet-sucks and being sick all night.

Uncle Bob was a power in local politics, of what party I do not know or care, and I suspect the same applied to him. As a result, he sat on the bench, and he took us along to observe a session over which he was presiding on the afternoon of the day we arrived to stay. When I was considerably older, I watched my other Uncle Bob sit as a petty judge, and had trouble understanding the bases of his decisions until my father pointed out that they were rigidly rooted in total partiality. Real Uncle Bob's conduct of his cases, by contrast, was completely fair, but bore as little relation to the law as did his namesake's. I never make the common mistake of confusing the meanings of words 'disinterested' and 'uninterested'; I simply remember how Uncle Bob was the former with respect to bias, and the latter in relation to the evidence.

The session was on the Friday; the next day he took us in his car on a tour of the country along the English side of the border. He kept telling us how lovely it all was, how quaint the villages, how jolly the pubs, how neat the thatch, what fun the churches, who had slaughtered whom, where, when. Some day I must go back to that area and absorb a dose of its undoubted delights, relish its rural relics, imbibe its beer, survey its spires, and greet its ghosts, but on that day the drive was a disaster for three reasons.

Firstly, as children of seven, eight and ten, we were simply not interested in the beauties of the countryside. Churches were simply places we had to go to on Sundays; thatch looked itchy; we weren't allowed in the pubs. And like all healthy young animals we were too absorbed in the excitement of our present to be impressed by other people's pasts. Secondly, it rained solidly all day with such malevolence that a step outside the car meant an immediate soaking. This intensified the third problem, which was a cumulative queasiness in tummies made tender by over-indulgence, then shaken soundly by the soft springing of Uncle Bob's American automobile.

Happily, my mind has drawn a veil over most of that day, dulling the details and the embarrassment of memory, but the reality cannot have been very jolly. What I do remember is my father trying to tide over the tedium of the final stages by organizing a game of Car Cricket. Uncle Bob had never played before, so we explained the rules. He was taken with the notion and insisted, as host, in taking on the rest of us, confident no doubt that his knowledge of the localities through which we were travelling would give him a comfortable edge.

Car Cricket is only one of the names of this game, and it is simply one of the many ways of building up a numerical score by keen and involved observation of the passing scene from a moving vehicle. The rules vary with the traditions of the family. In our case each side selected eleven players (present, past, distant, or mythical), and the score was determined by the names of the public houses passed as we went along. Scoring systems can be very complex; I travelled sometimes with a family who had a notebook in the glove compartment containing twenty-eight pages of detailed statutes and precedental rulings. They spent most of their time fighting over these, and missed most of the pubs. Travel in that car was like being at the bottom of a rugger-scrum in a Babelonian Bedlam. Julie-Anne, the eldest, later underwent a partially successful sex-change operation and is now a popular political pundit – almost inevitable, really.

Our system was much simpler: any limb was a run, any head a wicket. We stuck pretty rigidly to the wording of the name. Thus 'The King's Arms' yielded two runs without cost, while 'The Queen's Head' was a duck, but 'The Duke of Malborough' did not specify sections of his anatomy, and so clocked up 4 for 1. If the wording was ambiguous, the picture on the pub sign was taken as the primary interpretative authority. 'The Horse and Hounds' is numerically vague, but if the painting showed a mounted huntsman with eight dogs, your whole side was gone for 38.

Within even such a firm formula there is ample room for argument, and the game would be the duller without it. Here are a few which have cropped up in our contests. I am sure you will have met with similar ones, and have your own favourite family feuding points.

1. 'The Dog and Duck' – are wings limbs within the meaning of the Act? Is it 6 or 8 for 2?
2. 'The Angler's Rest' – one wicket and four runs for the fisherman, but how about another wicket and five more runs for the head, foot, and legs of his bed?
3. 'The Golden Bough' – is the branch of a tree a limb? If you allow that it is, what price 'The Royal Oak'?
4. 'The Volunteer' – the soldier himself surely counts 4 for 1; but the sign shows him bearing arms – a rifle and a sword – and do they count for two more runs?

The match in Uncle Bob's car ran a relatively simple course most of the way home. It didn't move very swiftly, for we were heading into twilight when we started, and the latter stages were played out in total darkness. We had to rely on picking out pubs in the head-light beams, and at the furious pace Uncle Bob drove that was not easy. The game developed in the way they always did with him – towards his full and obvious defeat. This was partly because he was driving, and could not put his whole mind to the play, but that cannot have been a major handicap, for it was obvious that very little of his mind was ever devoted to his driving.

The factors that ensured his downfall were exactly those involved in most defeats suffered by military commanders: failure to grasp the implications of the rules of the game, incompetence in applying those he did understand, and plain bad luck. Thus he did not bother to claim anything for 'The Old Mill', although the sign showed it was of the wind-powered type and worth four good runs. He failed to appeal when we passed 'The Railway Engine', when the sign clearly showed it to have a full head of steam, and his middle order was destroyed by a representative segment of the area's extraordinary enthusiasm for the post-Reformation Fitz-ducal explosion.

My uncle's temper came under increasing tension as his wickets tumbled while his total failed to mount to match ours. It broke when my father stretched the rules to the limit, and took his ninth man with the head on 'The Pint of Wallop'. He could not walk away from this game, as he was driving and we were still some miles from home. He switched off his headlights, and drove very fast on sidelights only, cutting about from one road to another, jamming on brakes and swirling into three-point turns, circling roundabouts completely, slamming to a halt halfway down a village street and reversing rapidly to find an escape route – all to avoid the slightest sight of noddle or pate.

This random manoeuvring took us miles out of our way. We had not been sure where we were when the mad dash started, and after twenty minutes of it we had no idea. To this day I do not know our precise position at the moment when Uncle Bob stood the car on its front bumper and yelled triumphantly 'Of course! Now I've got you!' At this he plunged the car into a dim network of streets which had the air of backing onto docks. I remember a vague feeling of recognition, but it must have been Mersey, not Clyde.

He seemed to overshoot what he was looking for. Suddenly he rammed the brakes on once again, reversed fifty yards, then swung left and continued, still backwards, still very fast, down a dark alley between tall buildings. I don't know what he had expected at the other end – we had given up expecting and taken to praying – but it surely wasn't to burst into a brightly lit and busy pedestrian piazza, scattering startled shoppers left and right until the car came to a halt under a large sign that said:

Your shopping spree
Is traffic free

In those days there were no breathalysers or blood tests, and one's fitness to drive was judged solely on behaviour and the way one answered police questions after arrest. Uncle Bob must be the only magistrate to lose his seat for 'driving backwards at forty miles an hour past a No Entry sign and across a No Vehicles Pedestrian Shopping Precinct while in no condition to be in charge of motorized transport'. I think the last part of the indictment was added on because of his rather incoherent statement to the apprehending officer that he was trying to find a pub called 'The Headless Centipede' in a village named Merrypuddle

Parvum, in order to clinch a cricket match of earth-shattering importance.

My third and final piece of legally-flavoured cricket is of more recent vintage. A few years ago I was called up on jury service, and went willingly with a sense of duty and the hope that the experience would obliterate the impression left in my mind when my school boarding-house matron, Miss (Midge) MacDonald, had similarly sat in judgment of the facts in a capital case in the High Court in Edinburgh.

'Guilty,' she reported to the House at tea after the opening day of the trial.

'Obviously as guilty as sin.' No evidence had yet been called.

'I can tell he is a man with blood on his hands by the way his moustache droops on one side.'

Luckily the poor wretch was found unfit to plead.

'Living the life of Larry in a hospital. A waste of the tax-payers' money. Should have been put down painlessly. Like a sick dog, he was; like a sick dog.'

That was for years her standard response whenever the topic arose (which, if she had anything to do with it, was frequently), even after fresh evidence came to light which proved conclusively that the demented fellow could not possibly have committed the crime. If Midge had had her way he would have hit the hemp for the hang of his hair.

So I went to the court in the hope that the jury system would prove as sound as the lawyers always claim it to be. I came away firmly conditioned into Goodly Living by the fear of ever finding myself on the receiving end of its justice.

There were eleven defendants facing four charges each. Eleven barristers spoke for them, a floating population prosecuted, and the case took eleven working days – a full calendar fortnight. The Law forbids me to reveal the details of the case, and to be honest I cannot remember them all that clearly now, but they were very complex and there were a lot of them. Two of the jurors, resentful at being called away from urgent business, paid not the slightest attention to the proceedings from the start, and conducted a marathon noughts-and-crosses contest throughout the entire case. The two ladies spent most of their time comparing notes on the subtle variations the female barrister wove within the severe strictures of subfusc, and the remainder wondering 'what on earth their mothers could have been thinking of'. At least four of the other jurers were overwhelmed by the third day, and gave in thereafter. The rest of us, though we tried, were to say the least a little muddled by the time the last of the fourteen partisan speeches had been poured over us.

I was worried. Mr Justice Jailem, presiding, was also worried, but for a different reason. He had two passions in his life at the time, one long- and one short-standing, and they were due to come most conveniently into conjunction on the Thursday, but that could well be the twelfth day of the trial unless he got it sorted out and tucked away on the eleventh. The Lord's Test opened that day, and he had a luncheon appointment in the Tavern restaurant with a certain Miss Kitty McShane, lately acquitted of grave social charges in his court, and now eager to prove her gratitude in his company.

I heard all that side of it later, after the good judge had resigned for reasons of health and the scandal had been successfully suppressed, from an ex-pupil of mine who had defected to the Arts post-A-level and occupied a humble niche in Mr Jailem's chambers. He also told me that Mr Jailem, though fond of the Law, and learned in it, was not passionately attached to it; it was this lack of passion which made him such a good judge, for obsessive love of the subject is a dangerous attribute in practising professionals. They become so bound up in the technicalities of their trade that they forget the people they are there to serve. Doctors devote themselves to disease and diagnosis, and make patients live up to their description; teachers toy with the trivia of transmission, and lose sight of the 'I' behind every pupil; lawyers let clients slip under while they balance happily on a log-jam of interlocking litigation.

'Ladies and gentlemen of the jury,' Mr Justice Jailem began his summing-up. 'This is a complex case, and I suspect that some of you have had trouble following it. It is, however, no more intricate than an innings in a cricket match. There are eleven batsmen, as it were; each of them has had a chance at the wicket, and has faced a number of deliveries. That the case has dragged on for ten days is a powerful comment on the extended run-ups employed by certain learned counsel. Would that I had the powers of limitation vested in the TCCB. It is not my job to comment on the standard of the bowling, which can be charitably characterized as varied, but I intend to take you through the match ball by ball, and to try to indicate how each defendant played his shots. It is for you to decide whether a particular player lost his bail or carried his bat, but it lies with me to interpret the Laws and call the no-balls.

He then proceeded to take us through the evidence in a brilliant and comprehensive analysis which, if unconventional in form, must have been sound in content, for there were no subsequent appeals. I discovered later in the jury room that four of us had filled in, independently, mock score-cards built up as he took us through the case. When we compared them, they matched exactly. That eventually settled the issue, for none of the other eight showed much interest, so the fate of the eleven accused was effectively decided by a sub-committee of four delegated by default. I think we probably got it right, but I doubt if that is the way it is supposed to be done, and I am sure it is not the way it ought to be done. It is of interest that the cricket carried into the verdict – ten of them went down, and only one came through with his record intact.

There was an intriguing sequel to all this only the other day. You know how one can be walking down a street and see someone approaching, partially recognize him, and be uncertain whether to stop and chat, or nod politely and pass on. This frequently happens to me as a result of my job and my terrible memory for names. It happened last Tuesday in the High Street. I saw a young man, in his mid-twenties probably, some distance away, and thought, 'I know you from somewhere, but what in blazes is your name, and what form were you in?'

I could see a glimmer of recognition in his eye, too, so I prepared to launch into my usual opening gambit on such occasions, the gentle leading question that is designed to dig out the data that might trigger a fuller memory: 'Hallo there. How nice to see you again. Can't remember when last I saw you. And what have you been doing recently?'

For some blessed reason I decided not to stop. So did he. We smiled, nodded, and passed on our ways. It was not until I was a good fifty yards further on that I recalled with horror our relative positions when last I saw him, what I had said, and what he must have been doing since.

I had been standing in the Foreman's place in the jury-box.

He was in the dock.

I said 'Guilty'.

Three and a half years.

Book Cricket

IT IS SIMPLY NOT TRUE that my deep suspicions of Eng. Lit. (Pound Onwards), which I admit verge on the pathological, stem from a disturbing encounter with an encyclopaedia salesman experienced by my mother while carrying me.

They can, in fact, be traced to a cricket match played in the Lower IVth Common Room on or around 24th June 1948, between Junior Remove 3 and their deadly rivals, Junior Remove 1. I was privileged to be a member of R3, as fine a group of young men as you could hope to find preparing themselves for the Great World Outside. There were eighteen of us. Later on, one played at Murrayfield and got on the Board of ICI; one played at Lords, and got a seat in the Cabinet; one played the Stock Exchange, and got eight years; and another played around in Prince Albert Park, Inverleith, and got married early.

R1 was a bunch of drips, swots, and similar non-sporting layabouts who got 104% in Latin tests and were rumoured to read poetry for pleasure. This last we found disturbing. We had not yet heard about Parisian ladies in leather boots, but at that age it was the approximate equivalent. It seemed as odd to us as getting your kicks from late Beethoven quartets. I must admit to deriving great enjoyment nowadays from two of those three stimuli, but as one ages the senses become more refined, or jaded, depending on one's outlook and to which of them I am referring.

You may be wondering what possible connection there can be between the Noble Game and Literature? This is a fair question, not fully answered by the undoubted fact that there is a considerable body of fine writing on the subject, and a significant proportion of players who can read it.

The link lies in the nature of a particular version of the sport. While bearing little physical resemblance to the real thing, it has the great advantage that it can be played under conditions which would seem to be impossibly adverse. The match I mentioned earlier, and which I shall describe in some detail later, took place during a closely supervised Preparation double period; its great value is emphasized by the fact that the players were held back at the end and publicly commended by the master-in-charge for the obvious intensity of quiet concentrated effort we had been applying to our work. Adult life has taught me that the game is equally valuable for situations such as committee meetings, sermons, theatrical performances, concerts, and any kind of supervisory activity. The key requirement is that reference to a book of some sort (minutes, Bible, script) should be acceptable and even laudable.

The method of play is as follows: to each letter of the alphabet a score is assigned. Thus, A stands for 1, B for 2, C for 3, up to 6 and then starting again, to the end of the alphabet. First, however, certain key letters are agreed to represent appeals; their choice is subject to local variation, but it is customary to pick four letters which commonly come at the end of sentences, such as D, R, S, and Y. Once accepted, each of these now means 'Howzat?'

Finally, each type of punctuation is equated to a method of dismissal. So, a full stop might be bowled, a comma caught, a question mark lbw (considering the manner in which most batsmen receive such a verdict, a significant linkage). In our games, exclamation marks were stumpings, semi-colons were run-outs, inverted commas were hit-wicket, while the infrequent full colon was obstruction (we were too young to appreciate the medical pun in this).

All this had to be codified and recorded before the match; I give here a sample of how it might look, but it must be remembered that local custom is all-powerful in such matters; the imposition of a centrally decided and rigidly standardized set of rites can rapidly fossilize a sport as easily as a religion. *Ex cathedra* rule has as much long-term value as plaster of Paris.

A = 1	O = 3	! = stumped
B = 2	P = 4	; = run out
C = 3	Q = 6	" = hit wicket
D = Howzat?	R = Howzat?	: = obstruction
E = 4	S = Howzat?	(= retired hurt
F = 5 (with	T = 1	) = returned to bat
overthrows)	U = 2	(but only
G = 6	V = 3	possible
H = 1	W = 4	immediately
I = 2	X = 6	after a
J = 3	Y = Howzat?	dismissal)
K = 4	Z = 1	... = umpire
L = 6	. = bowled	hesitant –
M = 1	, = caught	not out
N = 2	? = lbw	_ = no ball

A score sheet must now be prepared, with full teams written in, real or fanciful. A coin is tossed, the winning skipper selects a book, opens it at random, and his No. 1 takes strike on the first letter of the left-hand page.

Thus if I turn, as I frequently do, to the Scriptures, and they open at Romans III, 6, I find the following:

God forbid: for then how shall God judge the world?

Following the table provided, you may see the score developing in this way:

A. N. Other	6. 3. Howzat? (not followed by punctuation mark – not out). 5 (Temper!). 3. Howzat? (ditto – not out). 2. 2. Howzat? (obstruction – out) ....21.
N. Extman	5. 3. Howzat? (not out). 1. 1. 4. 2. 1. 3. 4. Howzat? (not out). 1. 1. 6. 6. 6. 3. Howzat? (not out). 3. 2. Howzat? (not out). 6. 4. 1. 1. 4. 4. 3. Howzat? (not out). 5. Howzat? (lbw – out) .... 81.

And so on.

You can see how a free-scoring and eventful innings is unfolding, full of innocent interest and exemplary excitement. I hasten to point out that it is also packed with material of intense academic value, embracing as it does the disciplines of spelling, grammar, syntax, punctuation, mathematics, and linguistic analysis.

When modern Biblical scholars explain how they use computers to tot up the frequency of key letters in Old Testament books, and thus prove that Isaiah was really written by at least two different people, Book Cricket players all over the civilized world know at once the strength of their arguments. How else can you explain the way he starts off so hesitantly in Chapter I, switches to a swift-scoring, big-hitting style solidly all through Chapters II to XII, then goes to pieces completely in Chapter XIII?

Of course, tricky problems can arise in interpretation, and have to be referred to an umpire. One I met with relates to the very passage I quoted above. In my last term, our Chaplain (nicknamed Dago for reasons to become obvious) tried to rouse our interest by teaching us a little Spanish, using the New Testament as a reader. We thought its likely usefulness as a phrase book for holidays on the Costa Blanca limited, so spent the translation periods playing somewhat roudy cricket matches (his class discipline was benign-tending-to-moist, and we had by this time adopted the normal adult Christian response when faced with the other cheek – we hit it even harder).

Following the Dago's instructions, we consulted El Nuevo Testamento, and found that Romans III, 6 reads:

No lo quiero Dios: . . .¿ Porque (etcetera)?

Now that posed some really ticklish teasers: look at the end of the first phrase. I am sorry to report that our collective reaction to this delicate interpretative dilemma was a doctrinally diverting though unsportsmanlike punch-up, which led us before the Ultimate Umpire – the Rev. J. R. Hook, MA, DPhil (Bill to those who were at risk from his cutting edge): the Head Master.

He sorted us out with his usual mixture of withering power and impressive scholarship: 'You are all gated for three weeks, and deprived of VIth form privileges for the rest of the term. This punishment is partly for the minor riot in a Religious Instruction period, but mainly for your demonstration of an appalling ignorance of a major turning point in English Social History.

'The problem you faced is patently a reverse of the famous Len Hutton Compulsory-Reply-to-Appeals Case. You will recall that in a certain Test match he played well forward, got a thin edge, and was struck on the pad. He bent down and picked up the ball, spent at his feet, to throw it back to the bowler. As he did so, the latter appealed in the usual manner, presumably for leg-before.

'Now, by cricket custom, an appeal is merely a request to the umpire to declare whether a batsman is or is not out, without specification of offence. In Hutton's case, the umpire rightly judged him not out in respect of the lbw but had no alternative but to give him out for picking up the ball, this being technically an obstruction. The resulting row nearly led to the expulsion of the Southern Hemisphere from the Empire.

'The reverse occurs here. The batsman survives an appeal initiated by the Deity, takes a quick single next ball, then tries to clip one to mid-wicket off his toes; the ball straightens a bit off the seam, hits his back leg, and skips down through fine leg for an easy two runs. He goes for a dicey third, and makes it home, but jostles the keeper on the run in.

'The keeper appeals for obstruction (S followed by colon).

'The umpire hesitates, then gives him the benefit of the doubt (. . .): not out on obstruction.

'But he must now consider the prior impact of ball on pad, and gives the batsman out lbw(;).'

I have never since been surprised at the most complex, detailed, and far-flung of Biblical exegeses. If old Bill Hook could cut a swath like that using one sentence of a bad Spanish translation of an almost meaningless Pauline outburst, how can I criticize even the wildest of clerical phantasies woven tenuously from the standard fifteen or so verses of text normally presented from the lectern?

The masterly way he sorted out our problem helped me to understand how he coped with his own when, later that year, he went South to take over one of England's great Playing-Fields-with-School-Attached. In the first week he found himself having to explain to the Customs and Excise a flourishing vodka still in the Chemistry department, and to the police a flowering relationship between his Vice-Master and a considerable body of the Brigade of Guards. I can think of certain portions of the Song of Solomon that might have helped him with both.

I am sure a man of his ability would certainly have assumed the mitre had he survived, but he fell victim to a frequently fatal fusion of success, limited vision, and a classical education. The classics gave him the success in the form of a best-selling work on 'Leg Theory in Ante-Bellum Tuscany'. With the profits he purchased an electric typewriter, which he insisted on wiring up himself. Daltonism reinforced classicism and led him to confuse red for green, and live for earth; he fried on the first shift-key, and came to an eternal full stop (upper case, one trusts).

But to return to the match between R3 and R1, and my aversion to Modern Writing. We had murdered them in every sort of physical game imaginable, while they had demolished us in any contest involving thought processes marginally beyond the capability of a backward baboon. For a final decider we agreed on Book Cricket, mixing as it does elements of sport and *litera scripta*. The rules were to be those laid out here, plus the condition, suggested by them, that each side should provide its own book, but with the other choosing the page. In our innocence we thought that a fair notion; we reckoned without the cunning of the intellectual and the depravity of the twentieth century novelist.

We chose Genesis (King James version) for our innings. They selected the last chapter and proposed that, to make it all doubly fair, we do the same when it came to their turn. Literary lambs that we were, we agreed happily to be shorn.

We also accepted a fixed-innings match – first period of the double to us, second to them – but this was normal practice in those days, long before grown-ups came to the idea that most captains are simply not skilful enough to organize an exciting finish if given too much time to play with.

Our innings went well. The final chapter of Genesis turned out to be just what we had come to expect of the Old Testament – not very thrilling, but solid stuff. This is true of nearly all of the Good Book, except maybe Proverbs, which tends to be a bit staccato. I cannot with any authority speak of the Apocrypha, which we of the Kirk viewed with grave suspicion; at that age we did not know why, but assumed it had to do with its scoring potentiality, and avoided it accordingly.

We had clocked up 786 for 9 by the end of the period. A respectable total, and we felt reasonably confident.

R1 presented their book. We were impressed, for it was published in France, though in English, and even in our proto-pubescent state we knew this meant naughty words. We turned to the last chapter, as agreed, and were completely shattered. I think it was the first time any of us had been truly shocked in our lives, certainly in the moral sense, though this was so severe it verged on the clinical. As we worked through the pages we were beaten by outrage into a jibbering catatonic schizophrenia – excited beyond response, depressed below repose.

There were naughty words, all right; some so naughty we did not know what they meant. There were detailed descriptions of activities we didn't know could happen, and couldn't understand how, or why. Unmentionables were not just mentioned, they were savoured.

But this was not what upset us. Children are not worried by mere words; they know they have no reality beyond what the reader assigns to them. There is no evil in words, only in the minds that use and abuse them; the same applies to bodies and bodily functions. What children see clearly as the ultimate threat, and therefore deeply shocking, is disorder, uncertainty; a lack of clear-cut rules, to be obeyed or broken, but there.

They also hate betrayal, and we had been betrayed; by R1, of course, but also by this dreadful book.

It was *Ulysses*, by James Joyce; a much-fingered Shakespeare edition. The last chapter is Molly Bloom's stream of consciousness – not so much a stream as a flood: in that edition fifty-six pages of close-packed verbiage without a single piece of punctuation the whole way through.

With no punctuation, no-one could ever be out. Their openers had scored 4,736 between them by the end of the period, and that was after only two and a half pages.

We never forgave R1, and I suppose all of us have gone through the rest of our lives convinced, with Benda, of *la trahison des clercs*.

I have read every word of Joyce I can get my hands on. I dislike his work and I distrust the whole school of writing he inspired. I like to pretend it is because of a hatred of chaos, a healthy scepticism over the possibility of genius without talent, of power without control, of beauty without form.

But I have a sneaking, niggling suspicion that it is really because in the last chapter of his second novel, in the last hour of the sixteen, he used hundreds of Ds, Rs, Ss, and Ys, and not a single .,;:?!(or '.

After all, for all our obsessions, the only part of the human anatomy which is really important to us is Face.

Liquid Cricket

THE ONLY REASON I was ever asked to play for the Freebooters was that they had to have one member of the club who knew the rules, at least well enough to wind up a match promptly and in a seemly manner if by any mischance it looked like lasting beyond six o'clock.

The Freebooters was our college drinking-cum-cricket club, very much in that order of precedence. I am told it no longer exists; I suspect this is not due to any general drop in the popularity of cricket, for none of the members (myself apart) actually liked the game, but rather because our present liberated young no longer feel they need to camouflage their excesses behind a pseudo-sporting screen of off-white flannel.

The college cricket captain was, by local legislation, *ex officio* Senior Pro of the Freebooters. They did not tell me this before they elected me, and it could well have been the reason why nobody stood against me. My naïve assumption that it was due to my obvious superiority in wit, charm, cricketing ability and leadership potential did not survive the first match of the season, and I have viewed elective office with grave suspicion ever since.

My college was not in the first rank socially, which means it had very few members with more money than sense. It did, however, have the usual small quota who, unable to match the filthy rich in means, thought it enough to ape them in manners. I am enough of a snob to believe that you have to be born with a true talent for unpleasantness, and these lads weren't really very good at it, so on the whole the proceedings of the cricket club were wholesome and innocent fun, though they bore but a tenuous relation to the Great English Summer Game.

All matches began promptly at 11.30 a.m. in 'The Queen's Head', a hostelry commendable in two outstanding particulars: it was practically inside the college, and it held ample stocks of Messrs Youngers' excellent beverages. In those days, loyal Scot though I was, I tended to agree with my English friends that the best way to view Tartan was through glass, and I fear that any respects I paid to my Scotch origins were mere lip-service.

We moved to the cricket field promptly at 2.30 p.m. This moderate urgency (the adjective is poorly chosen, for by 2.30 p.m. in 'The Queen's Head' moderation was a word with very little application) was imposed more by the licensing laws than any deep-seated drive to put willow to leather, and I well remember a match in which no play took place at all, due to a visit of Royalty to the city, which was marked by an all-day extension. Again I must correct myself; I remember very little of the match for the same reason, and it has since been my firm opinion that the influence of High Personages on the youth of this country is in general towards drunkenness and loose living, the latter stemming from my vague recollection of the subsequent highly sportive evening with certain ladies who shall remain forever nameless, mainly because they were nameless at the time.

The office I held in the Freebooters was that of Senior Pro. It was no sinecure, for it devolved on me to run the match completely on the field of play. This resulted from the nature of the office of captain, which was non-playing, for two very sound reasons. Only one captain in the history of the club had had any idea of how to play the game, and no captain had ever left 'The Queen's Head' in a fit state to play it, had he known how. To tell the truth, very few captains ever left 'The Queen's Head' at all.

The club motto was written on the fixture card, along with other vital information, like opening times, how to contact the nearest friendly pusher, and the going rate for bribing the club steward to keep the bar open after 1.00 a.m. The motto ran, 'Failure to score a run or hold a catch shall not be ascribed to moral obliquity,' and it was observed to the letter and in spirit, especially in spirit. Practice sessions were taken very seriously. They were held weekly in the college buttery, were run by a linguistics don and a University Gymnastics half-blue, and consisted of lessons in how to repeat 'She sells sea-shells on the sea-shore' while walking along a straight line after eight pints. (These were, of course, pre-breathalyser days.)

In later years I attained some fame (or notoriety) when as skipper of legitimate cricket sides I originated the all-round, multi-purpose, non-change field-placing system, which has saved many fielders unnecessary movement, and their captains unnecessary, and in many cases unwonted, thought. Until the introduction of my system it was considered essential to shift players about to compensate for the odd way in which the bowling switches from end to end about every six balls, and even to alter the field for each change of bowler. Nobody ever knew why this was done, for it never seemed to make any difference to the run of the game. However, while dismissing carefully planned, highly sensible and logical procedures which patently produce profitable results is commonplace in our society, it takes a bold man to disregard deeply ingrained totally pointless behaviour, and I would not have thought of doing so had I not been forced to perceive the beauty of the system during my time with the Freebooters. In their matches the field, once set, stayed set, for each player brought his pint onto the field with him, placed it at his feet, and would not thereafter move from that spot except for natural emergencies or refills.

Such rules as were observed were based loosely on the Laws of

Cricket, plus a few vital extras, the most invoked of which were as follows:

1. Any batsman scoring six or more runs in an over shall claim one pint, plus *pro rata* for surplus, from General Reserve.
2. Any bowler taking a wicket shall claim a pint from General Reserve.
3. Any player holding a catch or otherwise dismissing a batsman shall claim a pint from General Reserve.
4. Any player or spectator deemed by audible acclamation to have performed any meritorious act shall claim one pint from General Reserve.

I should at this point explain that the only officer of the club other than Captain and Senior Pro. was perhaps the most crucial, and certainly the most highly regarded. The holder's function was to make sure that adjacent to the field of play there was an adquate supply of essential equipment, such as beer and glasses, both of which tended to have a short life span. The title this officer held was 'General Reserve', which was appropriate, for he spent much of his time in consultation with our major supplier, the local brewery. The Senior Pro. looked after the minor stuff like bats, balls, pads and stumps. We never used bails, for by mid-afternoon few of the players could get them to stay on, and in any case some of the senior members did not like to be reminded of their current position *vis-à-vis* the local bench.

We played four matches during the term; the number was limited by rate of recovery more than anything, but an important factor was a shortage of clubs that played the Freebooter type of cricket. Two of our opponents were villages deep in the hinterland, seldom visited by outsiders, riddled with incestuous inbreeding, whose standard of play was so low they didn't notice what sort of odd game we played. In any case their local-brewed ale had a specific gravity that flattened any differences of style after three overs or two rounds, whichever was the earlier (a matter not easy to predict).

These two came early in the season, and were regarded as bracers or pipe-openers for the two big contests. The first of these was against a touring side of theological students from a Scottish university. To those not in the know it may seem strange that candidates for the Ministry of the Kirk should be playing cricket at all, never mind our sort of cricket. Others familiar with the student bodies north of the Tweed will confirm that two groups vie for the title of most bawdy, brawling and beer-sodden – the medics and the divines. Both are doomed to pass, with their finals, into instant incarceration in a straight-laced profession, in which not the slightest departure from narrow order is tolerated, either by their peers or their clients. They have to pack a great deal of deviation into a short student span, and most of them do a lot of packing of one sort or another. Those who played us were on tour not so much as a drinking-cum-cricket as a drinking-cum-anything team, and some of the anythings I witnessed while in their company were matched in my experience only by the behaviour of a Jesuit graduate student resident in the college, the most dissolute man I have ever known, whose social habits were darker than his clerical ones. Ecumenicity has since always seemed entirely logical to me.

The last match of the season (and my last for the Freebooters) was played against the Corsairs, a wild bunch of Fleet Street journalists, whose name referred partly to their attitude to life, and partly to their superb repertory of vulgar songs, whose *après*-match performances almost outdid their reefers in turning the clubhouse atmosphere blue. Although apparently anarchic, they showed firm organization in two vital matters: they were all present knocking on the door of 'The Queen's Head' promptly at opening time on the day of the match, and they always brought fourteen men to compensate for the three who would inevitably drop out (sometimes literally) before the first ball was bowled.

The year I played, the Corsairs were, as usual, polyglot, polychrome and, judging by the glint of single earrings, probably polyandrous as well: but not entirely, for there were camp-followers among their party, glamorous female followers. It was before the advent of the mini-skirt, but there was enough contour-hugging leopard-skin trousering about to suggest that following was not their natural *forte*. It struck me that day, and I have heeded it as a precept ever since, that alcohol arouses enthusiasm while reducing performance in more activities than cricket, and I fear that some of those London ladies ended that day's outing in semis in Surrey rather than flats *in flagrante*.

Looking back, I pride myself that my swan-song was a signal success. The details of the afternoon's play need not concern us here, and I must confess they hang a little hazy in my mind, but the opposition's penultimate wicket fell with the matching ball, and their eleventh man was forced to the crease. Actually, he was their fourteenth man, but numbers eleven, twelve and thirteen had stayed to keep our skipper company in 'The Queen's Head'. We had taken this as a piece of singularly good sportsmanship, though I suspect that the fact that none of them could stand upright at the time had something to do with it.

Forced is the exact word, for their last man was a huge coloured American of evil aspect. His amateur entomological interests had led him to believe that the outing was some sort of eccentric English grasshopper drive. He looked as if he had sprung from gang-leadership in the Bronx, but we discovered later that he wrote an agony column in a Dutch version of *The Tatler*, under the name of Aunty Juliana. It was published in Haarlem, so he claimed he was only one letter removed from his natural environment. He was wearing a combination of pink slacks and canary T-shirt which would have scared off a swarm of locusts, but the Freebooters were not consciously severe on matters of dress; to be honest, by that stage in the game they were not particularly conscious of anything.

A cluster of his team-mates persuaded him to the wicket at stump point, then retired leaving him standing, bat on shoulder, facing the square leg umpire, and shouting, 'Pitch, brother, pitch!'

The bowler (who was our No. 14) threw the ball at his head. He struck it towards mid-wicket, hurled his bat down on his stumps, and took off towards cover point. The ball smashed mid-wicket's beer glass, and he, infuriated, hurled it towards the bowler's end. A mite high, it hit the umpire between the eyes; he staggered down the wicket and collided with Aunty Juliana, who was heading cross-pitch for second base. They then became entangled with three converging fielders and the other batsman, all suffering from acute inebrial herd-instinct. They tumbled into one glorious tangle of legs, arms and beer-bellies, with the ball irretrievably trapped underneath.

This was just the sort of complex cricketing *impasse* I was there to sort out. I summoned all my extensive knowledge, tact and sporting instinct, and gave both batsmen out for obstruction.

The two sides accepted my decision without rancour. Actually they didn't pay much attention to it, for the pavilion clock stood at 6.01 p.m., and they were all walking off the field, their minds no longer on the game. The American's Texan girlfriend summed it all up rather well – his actions, the match, youth, perhaps life itself – when she greeted him at the boundary with the raucous comment, 'Ah don't know what you done, Honey, but you sure-thing done it wrong!'

Groundsman's Cricket

IT IS SAID that William Makepiece Shorter, London's last Publick Headsman, disapproved of capital punishment because it took the edge off the axe and made a right bloody mess of the block.

This was an early example of the self-centred and short-sighted attitude of Producers towards Consumers which led inevitably to the commercial decline of this country over the following century and a half. At the time, it was rare. Britain was deserting insularity for an emerging empire; red was spreading all over the globe, and black all over the account-books. In those days an Englishman would sell anyone anything, whether he wanted it or not, usually flinging in an unworkable system of government and a totally alien religion, also whether wanted or not. These bonuses were balanced by the imposition on the buyers of convicted criminals from our Lower Orders and idiot younger sons from our Upper Classes. The latter ensured that the Empire they were sent to govern disintegrated in decent disorder more quickly than most, while the former built nations of greater power and potential than ever emerged before from such a collapsing system.

The attitude is now all-pervasive. Have you recently

1. been unable to purchase an item on show in a shop window 'because it would spoil the display?'
2. been told that a vital spare part for a very common domestic appliance is no longer produced 'because there is no demand for it?'
3. been refused service of tea in a restaurant at 4.30 p.m. 'because we're laying out for dinner?'
4. been treated by your child's school as a trouble-making intruder with no right to interfere with his education?
5. been given the impression by a civil servant that the state he represents is an entity totally detached from, and with needs completely contrary to, those of its citizens, particularly you?

If not, you and I must be living in different countries.

Of course, we are all guilty of this entropic error. Once we have made something, organized something, created our little bit of order, we like to rest comfortable in it, and tend to resist its disturbance, because it means having to stir ourselves, create afresh, tuck in the ruffled edges.

The trouble arises, I suspect, from our lack of self-confidence, both personal and collective. Once we have succeeded in some task, however tiny, we are never certain of being able to succeed in it again. From the cradle to the grave, it seems downhill all the way; voices break, nerves crack, joints creak, sight and breath shorten, waists fill, chins double, energy dissipates. We are never again what we were, and what we were wasn't all that impressive. So we set up our little piece of perfection, be it a sharp axe or a tidy window display or a neat front parlour, and God help any one who tries to mess it about.

Arthur Sunlight was the groundsman at my college sports field, and he had two ambitions in life; the first was to produce superb cricket pitches, and the second to prevent people playing on them. Before you reject this combination as at best unlikely and at worst impossible, consider the well established fact that it is often those very parents who put most into preparing their children for adulthood who are most reluctant to release them into it. It is easier and less painful to cut an umbilical cord than an apron-string.

The pitches were Arthur's babies, and the outfield their nursery; great heavy stomping men with studs in their boots were about as welcome there as they would have been in the Special Care Baby Unit at the local maternity hospital.

In the first of his ambitions, he was wholly successful: it was generally accepted that the wickets on our ground were the best in the county. They played true and fast, and lasted well through a whole game – our Organ Fellow (an enthusiastic player who liked to pull out all the stops at about No. 7) called them Semi-Wenceslas Wickets: short and crisp and even.

Arthur Sunlight was utterly dedicated to the care of his cricket ground (we thought of it as ours, but all sports-ground users suffer from the same absurd delusion). He seemed to be there at all times. If you nipped in on the way to breakfast to collect your boots for an away match, there he was on his knees, trimming the grass with nail-scissors or winkling weeds with a hat-pin. Late into the evening, he was still at it, caressing next day's strip with a hand-pushed cutter that was to most lawn-mowers as wet-shaving is to electric hairclippers. Rumour had it that every blade of grass was numbered – certainly every pitch on the square was known to him by name, together with its fancies and foibles.

'You'll be on Arabella tomorrow,' he would say. 'That's allus assumin' it don't blow up snow. She jest 'ad to 'ave that dress o' red marl last Whit-tide, with a sprinklin' o' that there supry-phusphity that's took 'er fancy. It'll hold 'er quiet early on, but if you keep at 'er she'll move about a bit later on, an' she could get right lively early evenin'.'

The outfield was like a bowling-green. It had the look of Wembley on Cup Final day, or the Centre Court at the start of Wimbledon. When he was in a high good humour, as when poor weather had prevented play for several days, he could be seen rubbing his gnarled palm over the lush turf in an almost erotic action, cooing gently. We sometimes wondered whether what he sprinkled was fertilizer or talcum powder. He was the only man I have ever heard of who fitted headlamps to a light roller, and when some of us had a whip-round and presented him with a waterproof miner's helmet with built-in battery beam he accepted it not as a cruel comment but as a useful utensil.

As to the second of his ambitions, he was less successful, but not for want of trying. Like all men involved in the growing of things, he worshipped the great gods Sun and Rain, but to these he added a third, Cancellation.

'That there rain cloud,' he would say, pointing to a tiny fluff of cottonwool in an otherwise clear blue sky, 'That there is a Thunderstorm in the making; be wadin' knee-deep in it be midday, you mark my words. No point in startin', really.'

Instead of the more usual team photographs round the walls of the pavilion, Arthur had mounted cuttings showing Great Weather Maps of the past twenty-five years, all of them looking as if some celestial sphere music lover had overlaid the grooves of a long-playing record on the map of the British Isles, with the little hole in the middle slap on top of our cricket ground so that the water could pour through. People swore that he had trained the covers so that if you so much as sneezed near them, they started up by themselves and headed out towards the square. To be safe, we always advised visitors not to lean on them with sweaty palms.

In my last year at college, old Arthur was getting positively paranoiac about his pitches, but now he had good reason, for the agents of their ultimate, inevitable and total destruction could be seen encircling and encroaching upon the immediate environment. Our field was then on the edge of town, set in deep meadowland; dreaming spires looked over the pavilion roof at one end, and dozy cows over the hedge at the other. The whole tract was owned by another college, and the previous year its Master, playing Town/Gown politics, had traded them for the knighthood his wife coveted even more than the sort of mink coat that had recently appeared on the college Mistress. As our Rector said, 'It is only fair that of the two ladies in his life, one gets a rich covering on her back, where she earned it, while the other gets a handle to her name, for keeping such a tight grip on him for thirty-five years.'

As a result of the deal, a motorway by-pass was to be driven straight through these lovely pastures, obliterating two pleasant villages, three quiet inns, and the cricket grounds of two other colleges as well as ours. In doing the deal with the Local Authority and the Ministry, the Master had broken faith with the villagers, the farmers, the innkeepers, and the other colleges, who had all trusted his word when he promised to care for their interests in return for their loyal support. They should not have been surprised, for to a politician loyalty is primarily a commodity to be exploited, and only secondarily a virtue commanding respect.

Now bulldozers had chased the cattle from the neighbouring fields, and digging dinosaurs had ripped great gashes in the grass, fouling the rich earth with pipes, wires, and concrete. The last game of the season would be the last played on that ground, until travellers began dicing with their lives in the popular family sport of Motorway Madness. Our matches were monitored by mighty machines waiting watchfully over the weekend. It depressed us; as will be seen, it drove Arthur to distraction, a place well known in psychiatric circles to be located just a short distance round the bend.

That final match began in conditions that were cloudy but dry; within an hour, a persistent drizzle developed. At the first drop, Arthur started hopping about on the boundary, edging the covers over the line, hinting with broad sweeps of his arm that the players should be moving into the pavilion, and off his sacred turf. Normally we would have been only too happy to comply, for we were all of us fair-weather cricketers. I cannot understand the enthusiasm some people show for shivering through a supposedly summer sport in anything short of, and sometimes including, sleet and snow. I am sure it is a modern perversion, certainly not pre-victorian, a sort of twisted assertion of masculine impermeability. In the Good Old Days it was considered fatuous to try to continue outdoor leisure pursuits such as bowls or battue or battle when the weather turned nasty. Any fool knew that all the fun goes out of it when woods skid, or game stays sodden down, or rust gets into your tasset. A fellow simply could not hit his proper quota of jack or pheasant or peasant if the elements were unfavourable, so it was better to get back to a bit of indoor dalliance until the clouds cleared.

But our present situation was not normal; we badly wanted to finish this game. It was the decider for the college league table, and was against the very college whose Master had sold our ground from under our boots. What is more, although on past performance they were the better side, on this occasion we were in with a good chance, for on the previous day two of their star performers had been sent down for persistent behaviour of a most reprehensible, interesting, and almost impossible nature.

On top of that, considerations of damage to the pitch no longer applied, for by the next season the pitch would no longer exist, and more clover leaves would cover it than ever Arthur Sunlight would have tolerated, for one of the main motorway access points was planned for just that place.

So we went on playing, ignoring the increasingly suggestive, not to say seismological, gesticulations from the periphery. The rain got heavier, we got wetter and more determined, Arthur got more and more agitated. Eventually he could stand it no longer, decided to take matters into his own hands, and pushed the first of the covers straight on to the pitch. Since play was still in progress, this involved mowing down two slips, the wicket-keeper, the batsman on strike, and the rather silly backward point much favoured by our freshman classics scholar, who rather fancied his chances with leg-breaks pitched on middle-and-off. Luckily, the cover was an affair of canvas and wire on a light aluminium frame, so little harm was done to anything other than white flannel and dignity.

There was a pause while the captains conferred. We were the hosts, so their skipper left it up to ours. Out of courtesy, he consulted the batsmen, but they were quite happy to continue in conditions in which the bowlers could not grip the ball properly and had to shorten their run-ups, while the chances of a catch being held had dropped from the usual low to absolute zero. Our man rallied his troops, we pushed the cover back off the pitch, and got on with it.

Within two minutes the cover was back again, this time pushed in front of the tractor, driven by a grim-faced and implacable Arthur. When the two slips, keeper, batsman, and rather silly backward point had crawled out from under it again, we found that the groundsman had departed, leaving the tractor immobilized in some fiendish fashion, in the hope, no doubt, of blocking the removal of the cover. It was now pouring stair-rods, but both teams were by this time locked in their determination to carry on in the face of this obstruction by a mere mechanical. We lifted the cover to the edge of the field – an easy matter, for it was no great weight – took off its wheels, and those of its twin, and threw them among the clutch of beasts in the next field. We tried to lift the tractor out of the way, but it was itself a hefty brute, and the combination of its size and our sodden and slippery state defeated us; we left it where it was, and played on.

I must admit it was a bit odd having that tractor stuck there. It meant that in the first over the bowler had a run-up of eight and a half inches, while in the next the wicket-keeper had to sit on the front bumper. The visiting skipper insisted on applying the Law on Impedimenta with rigour, which was fair enough, for we were the side technically responsible for the obstruction, and it looked as if they were going to get a considerable contribution from this metallic twelfth man. We never discovered his full scoring potential because at the end of that over old Arthur broke cover from behind the sight-screen, galloped out to the centre, grabbed both sets of stumps, and headed out of the gate.

Both teams streamed after him in hot pursuit; out of the ground, left down the road to the High Street, and then in and out among the shoppers in that busy suburban market place. Halfway down, the traffic was being held up by a portly constable to allow a party of children to cross, and Arthur nipped across with them. We followed, and the startled drivers watched as twenty-two men in full cricket gear, two umpires in long white coats, and a few camp-followers poured across. The verb is well chosen, for we were soaked to the skin, muddied and bedraggled from our efforts with the covers and the tractor, while the heat of our chase could easily have been ascribed to intemperance, especially in a town not unfamiliar with student behaviour. The fact that among our followers was our own Rector, who because he was also Vice Chancellor *pro tempore* was dressed in full flowing academic robes, made little difference to their opinion, for they were familiar with his behaviour too.

We lost our quarry somewhere between Payne the Plumber's and the monumental mason's, so we straggled back to the ground, and took stock. We could not find a single stump anywhere, but the rain had eased to a steady torrent, and our determination had not let up one whit. There was a pair of Windsor chairs in the pavilion; one of the umpires found a saw, and we took the backs clean off and stuck them in the ground as wickets. They were a bit low and wide, and the lack of loose bails would no doubt have raised some problems of interpretation, but they were never put to the test, for just as the first ball of the resumption was about to be bowled, a terrible clanking clamour arose beyond the hedge.

When work had stopped for the weekend on the previous evening, a group of men had been laying a main sewer, and one of the huge sections of pipe was left dangling as from the beak of one of the high-necked monsters. From the way it was now nodding its head, and judging by the boiling gasses venting from its rear end, it was obviously on the move. As its huge caterpillar tracks crushed the hedge and bridged the shallow ditch, we caught a glimpse of Arthur Sunlight in the driving seat, heaving at the controls with what seemed to be less than confident and practised ease.

The great beast ground its slow passage across our field, straight for the square, as players scattered before it. It jerked to a halt just short of the wicket, its head with the suspended pipe section poised directly over the middle.

Whether by accident or design, Arthur pulled the release lever, and the man-high cylinder of earthenware dropped twenty feet on to the pitch. It shattered, but not before it had dug a groove nearly a foot deep, a yard wide, and stretching clear across the wicket. Luckily no one was underneath, but that was the end of the match, the wicket, and the ground.

In a Phyrrhic way, Arthur had won.

I still have the score-book; written boldly across the uncompleted page is the following:

MATCH ABANDONED — DRAIN STOPPED PLAY

Cupid Cricket

I HAVE NOTHING AGAINST SEX – it seems to me an excellent way of meeting people – but I get annoyed when it interferes with really important things like sport and sleep.

Strictly speaking, it seldom does, for sport is usually carried out in costumes, places, and at times which make clashes unlikely, if not downright perverse, and as for sleep – well, whoever heard of anyone wanting to extend the entrée into the period proper to coffee and liqueurs?

Love, however, or rather, Falling in Love is another press of emotions entirely. The English are notoriously bad at sorting out their personal relationships – I speak with the detachment of a Scot, a race reputed to be incapable of forming them at all – and their language reflects this in the lack of clarity allowed to the word love and its derivatives. For our present purposes, let me define the terms in medical phraseology without, I hope, clinical obscurity.

Love is a chronic and progressive condition; once well established, it gradually takes over one's whole life, altering attitudes, colouring perceptions, forcing irrevocable commitments, claiming hostages to Fortune. Its grip gradually engrafts two personalities one on to another until it would be more meaningful to describe *them* as 'single' rather than the merely unwed. Most people don't know they've got it till they've had it for a long time. They can, however, recognize its symptoms, for these are obvious to any observer: love cures, love heals, love supports. It enriches pleasure and ennobles pain; it makes all that is past worthwhile, and the future a rich prospect. It is an expression in human terms of the principle that forced God into Creation – that experience is without meaning unless it is shared.

Falling in Love, on the other hand, is an acute and transient affliction, it strikes like a fever, and shows many of the same symptoms: panting, sighing, sweating, hallucination, disorientation, anorexia, insomnia, irritability, and loss of concentration on anything but the causative agent.

It is this last aspect that is illustrated in this tale, and the memory was summoned the other day by the sight of an old Cricket Club Treasurer's receipt which fell out of an ancient score-book. I opened the book at the pages it had been marking, and there it all was, flooding back out through the pencilled hieroglyphics.

At my first place of employment there was a flourishing staff cricket team, and I played for it nearly every Tuesday evening. We played mainly village sides, but also the local West Indians, rare in those days, and our deadly rivals, the opposition firm's Social Club. I don't think I have ever found cricket more routinely enjoyable than in those regular village matches. We weren't very good, but then neither were they, so the games were hugely agreeable on a happily incompetent level. A lot of wickets fell because of the batsmen, and a lot of runs got scored because of the bowlers, but the scoreboard didn't give that away, and the ladies didn't know the difference, so who cared? As a bonus, the local rag reported the contests as if they were of first-class county status, and our children believed what they printed, at least until the normal onset of total lack of respect, which seemed to come much later then than now; these days the concept of 'bumbling idiot' replaces that of 'hero-figure' at about the same moment that jeans replace rompers.

Most of our games were of little consequence, which is how games should be, at least at the level I play them. Treating life as if it is a game may well remove some of its sting, but treating a game as if it is life removes much of its point, and replaces it with needle. The only matches into which some of this seriousness crept were those involved in the contest for the Infirmary Cup, a knock-out charity competition between all the local sides, the climax of which was a final in the town park, which attracted a big crowd for the collecting boxes and much kudos for the winning team.

We treated the early rounds of the competition as if they were ordinary matches of no special significance, but that year we did well, won steadily, and progressed into the later stages, where the whole atmosphere began subtly to change. Partly it was our own inflated egos; to be regarded as big frogs was passing pleasant even if we knew that our little pond was but a drop in the cricketing bucket.

Partly, also, it was Pressure from Above; not the heavenly, but the Head Office variety, which for most of us at that stage in our careers was rather more authoritative. To give them their due, most of the time Management kept out of our hair down at the club. They coughed up the subsidy that kept us going, without complaint, even eagerly – I suspect they clawed it back as Permissible Expenses from the Inland Revenue (that is, us; and, of course, you). But they soon took an interest when we got through to the quarter-finals, and comments about 'the staff team of a Major Local Organization' began to appear in the rag (or, rather, rags; in those days there were three weeklies in the town. Now there is only one, and all the drivel is concentrated into a single dose; harder to swallow, but it goes down quicker).

So it suddenly became important to win. It is, I suppose, always important to win; there is no fun in playing any game if you don't try to best your opponent, for is not sport simply a socially acceptable substitute for slaughter, a form of fighting with minimized injury, designed to channel and satisfy our aggressive instincts? If you doubt it, look at the words we use: even in chess we 'beat' the other fellow. The other day my ten-year-old niece promised to murder me next time – and she was only talking about Snakes and Ladders.

For most of us, most of the time, this aspect of sport is of peripheral importance. We enjoy having our primal urge in that direction massaged gently into indolent activity, but matters relating to other basic impulses tend to rank higher on our attention index. Thus if two players meet on the field in urgent consultation, they are least likely to be saying: 'We must strengthen our collective resolve and so struggle together that this our foe shall be utterly put down, and our Name emblazoned in the Halls of the Heroes.'

Much more likely is: 'Who's the bird on the long-on boundary?'

And most likely by far: 'Did you order a fresh barrel?'

It became a matter of some urgency that our run of wins be extended, at least for the next three cup matches, and we began, therefore, to try to determine what factor or factors it was that had led to our successes. Could it have been due to a general flowering of our middle-order batting, or an increase in the cunning of our spin bowlers? Or a spectacular sharpening in our performance in the field? It would have been nice to have been able to think so, but a glance through the season's score-sheets told another and much simpler story; there was one new element impelling us upwards from our habitual mediocrity, and one only – Bert Bigglesworth's bullets.

Bert had joined the firm the previous December, but it had not been until halfway through the summer that he mentioned that he 'swung the arm a bit'. We were always short of quickies, so we gave him a trial game. He proved able to swing his arm to very great effect indeed, dismissing the entire 'Fox and Hounds', Nether Pothole, side for 24, and all castled.

He was a mild, meaty man with a shambling walk and arms whose knuckles seemed almost to brush the ground. He moved slowly and with careful deliberation, mainly because he was so short-sighted that, even with his pebble-glasses on, anything beyond about five yards was a vague blur. He did not look as if he could get up enough steam to blow a penny-whistle, but when you put a cricket ball in his hand and pointed him in roughly the right direction, he flew up to the wicket with a purity of action that approached the poetic.

His first half-dozen balls were usually wides, but then he would begin to bracket them, and start bowling what one of his early victims in our part of the world christened his 'bullets', because they were very fast, and absolutely straight. This latter characteristic was the main ingredient of his success, and it bears out a theory I have developed about how to succeed in commonplace cricket. I call it McKendrick's Law of Inevitable Inaccuracy, and in informal layman's terms, it goes something like this: At all but the highest levels of any sport, the outstanding fact that is never articulated, and doesn't usually matter because all are affected equally, is that none of the players are very good at it. (There is an equivalent Law for the entertainments industry, called 'Inevitable Incompetence', which doesn't matter if you don't watch too much television, and one for the business world, entitled 'Inevitable Inefficiency', which does matter because of an important variation: the inevitability becomes more rigid higher up the hierarchy, not less.)

Applied to cricket, this Law rests on the following observable facts:

1. Every batsman misses, or fails to hit cleanly, a significant proportion of all the balls he faces. At the sort of level I am discussing, the figure fluctuates about two per over.

2. Of all the balls a bowler delivers, a significant proportion are off target; not, as many like to claim, by deliberate intent (few bowlers of this class have a very clear notion of where their next ball is going), but because accuracy is a random and not a controlled effect. At this level, an averagely well-thought-of bowler probably gets two balls per over on the wicket if he is lucky, and luck normally has a considerable part to play in it.

It follows logically that the rate of fall of wickets depends inexorably on the coincidence of balls missed with balls on target; to all intents and purposes, the only method of getting out of any real importance, and the one which should by rights most frequently appear in the score-book to explain a batsman's departure, is 'missed it', meaning bowled, lbw, or stumped, with perhaps 'nearly missed it', meaning caught. It also follows logically that the pattern to follow to achieve higher than average success is simple in theory, if a little harder in practice: batsmen must hit the ball more frequently, and bowlers the stumps.

Bert was like nearly all fast bowlers in his performance with the bat, that is, extremely haphazard if occasionally spectacular, but his rating on the bowling criteria established above was remarkably high. Once he got going, at least four balls in every over, and often all six, would be plumb on the wicket. Add to that the fact that they were pretty quick, and pitched on a good length, stir in the miss-rate normal for the batsmen at whom he was bowling, and you end up with a wicket nearly every over.

You may have noticed that there has been no mention of movement in the air or off the seam, of packed slips or leg theory, green tops or sticky dogs: in our sort of cricket these were of minimal influence in deciding the course of a match. This extension of my Law is upheld by two further easily verifiable observations

3. Most catches get dropped, especially in the slips, and
4. Most umpires are myopic, partially deaf, semi-comatose, and don't know the rules; they tend, however, to give out lbw on principle any batsman who allows the ball to hit his pads, and even they cannot easily reverse the decision implied in a shattered set of stumps.

Please do not think that I am trying to devalue the importance of these matters; they are minor only in their effect on the outcome of the game, not on its enjoyment. I once got sucked into a bridge group that met fanatically every Thursday evening. They informed me that this was the only really intellectual card game – a fascinating battle of wits, cunning, memory, and a fine feeling for fundamental principles. In the first few sessions I didn't understand much of what was going on, in spite of the eager aid offered, particularly by my opponents. So I bought a book, mugged it up, returned to the fray, and understood rather less. It took four more disturbing sessions before the penny dropped: all the players thought they knew the rules and systems, but they did so very imperfectly; they worked on the assumption that they could remember every card played, but on the whole didn't; and what knowledge they had, they applied with degrees of skill that varied from not too good to downright terrible. The outcome depended only very marginally on merit, and mainly on how the cards fell and whom you got stuck with as a partner. I went back to Scrabble.

But it didn't really matter that the players were getting ninety per cent of their pleasure from the apparent application of skills they did not possess to systems of play which were not in operation. They were enjoying themselves, and that was the whole object of the exercise. The same is true of commonplace cricket. A first change bowler comes on, consults heavily with his captain, and shifts everyone around until he has set an attacking field of five slips, gully, close point, third man, and a square cover. He then bowls six overs consistently wide of the leg stump, gets two caught off the top edge sweeping, and one lbw with the only ball that might have hit the wicket with a wide stretch of the imagination and a matching movement off the pitch. He is, rightly, deemed a great success, there is much debate afterwards on the technical nuances of his action, grip, run-up, and tactical sagacity, and a marvellous time is had by all.

So with Bert we had what amounted to an unfair advantage, a secret weapon. All the rest of us were trapped unchangeably at the same lowly level by a sort of sporting Original Sin – we all knew how to do it right but none of us could, so we pretended we did. Bert soared above this self-delusion, and for a while dragged us with him.

We walked through the quarter-final, brushed aside the opposition in the semi, and were all set for a great win in the final. Sweet it was going to be, and profitable, for the team that had struggled to the top on the other side of the draw was our old rival Industrial Dishcloths Inc. (Output and Transport Section), better known to us by the acronym. There were but two weeks and a couple of village games to go when disaster struck.

Bert fell in love; madly, passionately, besottedly. The girl was one Arabella Bottomly, but who or what she was did not signify, as I suspect it seldom does – love, as in 'falling', is not only blind, but deaf, dumb, and daft. The important point was the effect it had on Bert or, rather, on his bowling. He first saw his Arabella at the Saturday Hop down at the club, and by the following Tuesday had gone completely to pieces. He sat moping in the score-box all through our innings, staring vacantly out of the window with unseeing eyes. He didn't want to bowl, and when he did, we wished he hadn't. We lost for the first time in eight matches, and against the Nether Pothole lot, too (a return match).

By the next game, he was in an even more distressing state; interest, condition, and coordination completely gone, length and line all over the place, a mere shell of a man. We lost again, and that evening, at an emergency meeting of the Club Committee, I was charged with the vital task of sorting him out in the two days remaining before the big match. I got stuck with it because he and I both came from the North – to the inhabitants of the Home Counties, Manchester and Glasgow are approximately the same place; in truth, everywhere except the Home Counties is approximately the same place, and they always seem surprised to hear that life exists there.

I asked around, and discovered that Bert was so shy that he had not even dared approach the girl, let alone declare his interest. I also got the word from the distaff side of the shop floor that she was likely to be moved only by a declaration of Honourable Intentions (in those days the phrase had implications other than the laughable). I got to work.

On the Tuesday of the Great Match, two days later, there was delivered to Arabella's lodging a bunch of two dozen fine red roses, with a note, in Bert's hand, which read as follows:

> Like me you seek for life-long bliss;
> Here is a chance you must not miss.
> A secret lover pines for you;
> The score-box: Tuesday; half-past two.

It worked.

She turned up, he bowled like a man inspired, we won. Our skipper received the cup from the Lady Mayoress and promotion from the Area Manager. We all got a bonus, and I received an unofficial vote of thanks from the Club Committee for 'the exercise of my skills in the winning of this famous victory'. I bat No. 8, and we declared at 155 for 5. I was not called upon to bowl – Bert got them all – and I hardly touched the ball in the field. I therefore suspect the skills referred to were my moderate touch for doggerel verse, and my semi-criminal ability at forging hand-writing. The piece of paper whose fluttering-out triggered this tale must be unique in some way. It reads:

To Match Expenses: 2 doz. Red Roses...............7/6d

Intellectual Cricket

I HAVE A FRIEND who works in the brewing industry, and he told me the following which he swears is true. It seems that the really tricky bit in the whole process of brewing is knowing when to stop the barley germinating. Too early, and not enough sugar has been produced; too late, and the seeds begin using it up in sprouting shoots and roots. Until recently this decision was taken at his plant by a very old man who had been at the job man and child (and apparently in that order) for about a hundred and fifty years.

Things get critical on or around the eighth day, and from then on he would go to the Malting Floor every hour or so, pick up a handful of grains, rub them between palm and thumb, sniff them, listen to them (having first, some say, spoken to them), then throw them in the air and watch them fall. Nearly always, his face showed nothing, and he said nothing, shuffling silently out to return to wherever he othertimes went to do whatever he otherwise did – no one knew quite what that place and function were; certainly when he retired, nothing else was noticeably left undone.

Every once in a while, however, as the scattered particles drifted down, his features would crack slightly and he would utter an earthy 'Aaaaarrrghghgh', and you knew the moment and the crop were ripe. He never got it wrong, which is just as well, since a mistake would mean the loss of the whole batch.

About five years ago, new bright management installed automated computer-linked micro-sensor equipment that measured temperature, humidity, acidity, alkalinity, salinity, density, specific gravity, and fifteen other parameters which were totally irrelevant but came in the package, then switched on a panel reading 'READY' when it reckoned the germination was at its proper stage. They sacked the old man, shovelled in the first batch, and went about their busy executive ways with expectant grins on their fiercely infallible faces. These faded gradually over the next three weeks, and went completely when they noticed delicate green tendrils twisting round the edge of the still-dark panel.

They cleared out the healthy little jungle, and spread a new batch on the Floor. Now, the old method of stopping the germination was to pile up the grain into heaps, which trapped the heat and raised the temperature; this is labour intensive, and was replaced by underfloor electric elements switched on automatically by the cunning calculator signalled by the subtle sensory cells. After two days the second batch looked and smelt like roasting coffee beans, and they called the old man back. He now sits watching the dials, cathode-tubes, digital displays and pretty panels with interest ('Better thun telly'), then shuffles into the Malting Floor, picks up a handful of grain, rubs it . . . and says 'Aaaaaaaarrrrghghgh!'

There is a close analogy between that story and the way some people try to intellectualize cricket. A top-class captain inspects the wicket, looks at the sky, sniffs the air, feels the ache in his left big toe, and invites the other side to take first knock. Sometimes he gets it right and his openers have ripped a hasty hole in the opposition's upper order by lunchtime; sometimes wrong, and their Nos. 1 and 2 are fifty a piece in an hour. The successful skipper gets it right more often than wrong, but not by much. He weighs up consciously the factors he knows he knows about, and subconsciously some he doesn't, but the variables are so numerous and in many cases beyond prediction, that even if he comprehended and could measure them, it would take longer to programme the computer needed to handle them than it would to play the match.

At lunch, some idiot from the media buttonholes him and asks: 'Will you tell my readers/viewers/votaries how you conceptualize the integrated strategy which led inevitably to your telling tactical decision this morning?'

Since most top-class cricket captains are fairly intelligent men with well developed senses of humour, the reporter gets the sort of answer he deserves, and since, further, he doesn't realize what most sportsmen think most reporters deserve, he prints it word for word because as a professional media man he tends to be a bit short on words of his own, at least those with any worthwhile meaning.

The trouble is that the readers/viewers/votaries then take seriously the high-sounding nonsense supplied by the cricketer, not realizing that his slight speech impediment, which appears only when he is interviewed, is due not so much to nervousness as keeping his tongue firmly in his cheek. Of course, persistent heavy interviewing over a long period can result in tongue withdrawal symptoms, and we have all listened to or read the views of top sportsmen who have begun to believe what they are saying. Luckily, most of them do not succumb until they are at the tail end of or past their playing days, so the condition has little or no effect on the nature or conduct of the game, though it may on their friends.

I have no argument with those who seek, in their reporting, to sensationalize cricket or any other sport; they are merely doing their grubby little best to sell more newspapers, and their articles bear about as much relation to the sport they prey on as a column headed 'Vicar and Scoutmaster in Choir-school Exposé' does to theology, education, music, and the Duke of Edinburgh's Award Scheme. If you really think the trouble an England middle-order batsman has with his wife more interesting than that he has with accurate leg-spin, then the way you regard cricket is not mine, but you certainly get the press you want.

I am attacking those who try to read or write into the game a much more profound cerebral content than it deserves, can support, or, as far as the players are concerned, wants. Such people can be met in every human activity, and their motives are understandable; they are even excusable if subconscious, much less so if tendentious, for by establishing extreme depth in a subject they infer great merit in their ability to penetrate it. They have been at it since the first witch-doctor set up in business, and their continuing successful activity is demonstrated by the recent establishment at a major American University of a Department of Advanced Theoretical Needlework.

Cricket involves the brain, but the stem, not the cortex; it is a feeling, doing activity, not a thinking, theorizing abstraction. Of course, there is a place for induction, deduction, and dialectic; decisions have to be made, but the problems they pose proceed not from perplexity over perceptions, but premises. Any fool can decide which horse will win the Grand National, and many do; the logic is easy – it is the suppositions that are insecure. Similarly, it doesn't take a genius to decide whether to bat first or bowl; given the nature of the game, a genius is no better fitted to make the choice than a juggins, and captains with mentalities close to both extremes have led Test sides with almost equal success.

Most of the causal crises in cricket are crafted by the hand and eye of an Epstein rather than the brain of an Einstein. The former was once asked how he came to calculate the dimensions of the spaces his sculptures enclosed. His reply (roughly translated) was: 'Wherever it seems to need a big hole in, I bash one.'

A near-great bowler who during a long career for county and country gave much pleasure to those watching him, and trouble to those facing him, asked how he established 'the continuing dialogue between his delivery and the batsman's response' replied simply 'I let 'em go when I reckons it's the proper time, and from then on it's 'is problem.'

I went to school with the son of a Border farm who even in his teens was building the herd of Aberdeen Angus which has since brought him considerable wealth and an enormous reputation world-wide as a judge, perhaps *the* judge, of quality steak while it still has a leg at each corner. Some years ago he agreed to break his usual retiring habits and preside in the ring at the Smithfield Show. I was at the ringside when he was interviewed for television. The media pundit opened with the usual statement establishing his obvious equality with and probable superiority

[91]

over the expert being questioned, then asked: 'Tell us, Mr Todd, bearing in mind the total concept of dead-weight versus on-the-hoof comparisons, coupled with conversion ratio parameters, and in view of Ministry Guide Line No. 254 implementing the consensus opinion expressed by the Common Market Agriculture Authority in January of 1976 – how did you come to choose this animal as this year's Supreme Champion?'

His answer sums up my thesis: 'It's a nice wee beastie – I like it.'

The best writers on cricket – Glasgow, say, Cardus and Arlott – have never puffed up the pedantic nor inflated the intellectual aspects of the game. They may have gone overboard a bit at times on the environment, physical and sensory, but they described what had actually happened and tried with considerable success to make us feel we had been there, seeing it, hearing it, feeling it. There aren't many of that quality about (I don't suppose there ever were), and the bulk of sports reporting and commentary these days merely makes me glad I couldn't make it, while a high-powered minority does its best to impress on me that, had I been watching, I would have been unable to understand the unfolding of the creative conceits as the mysteries were celebrated by the performing priesthood. I watched a Sunday thrashabout on the box the other day. A fledgling bowler – his field, as is customary in these matches, spread all round the boundary, not a slip or gully in sight, keeper standing up – bowled six consecutive near-wides down the offside. The batsman swished symbolically at each one, and gratefully trotted his two byes. The Guru said at the end of the over: 'The plan here is obviously to cleverly trap him into hanging it out to dry and tickling it gently.'

Apart from the split infinitive, the misplaced adverb, and the clichés clashing in an unseemly manner, was I missing something?

To be fair, media standards in the cricketing arena are much higher than for other sports, and the particular level is at times remarkable. It seldom sinks to the absurdity of, for instance, football reporting. When I was a little lad, I kicked a ball about in the playground with a blond giant called Eric Little. He was a lovely fellow, patient, kind, gentle, fairly bright, and very, very strong. He got himself a diploma at the local college, and settled down to what has proved to be a highly successful and socially useful career as a primary school teacher. He was, fundamentally, a terrible footballer, because although he thought quite quickly, and produced good solutions to tactical problems, his limbs didn't seem to hear about them until they no longer had any relevance to the shifting scene around him. He had, however, one gilt-edged copper-bottomed asset: although most of the time he moved as if similarly encumbered, once every other match he would find the ball at his feet and would then hit it with one of them straight into the back of the net, frequently taking the goal-keeper with it. To a professional club manager, this was money in the bank, so Eric played for our nearest 1st Division side over quite a few years.

The crowd had doubts as to his abilities; they yelled things like 'Gi'e the big Jessie a yo-yo!'

Eric had no illusions about his skills. He said, 'As long as they pay me a great deal more for standing around doing nothing very much on a Saturday afternoon than I get for a lot of hard work the rest of the week, I'll carry on playing, but I certainly wouldn't pay to come and watch me play.'

The Press described him as 'This brooding presence, dominating the mid-field with his mindful menace.'

Were we all talking about the same person?

At the level I play, these problems seldom obtrude very seriously. We get the odd player who thinks he's God's gift to the Nether Sludgepond pace attack, has been for the past fifteen years, and damn well intends to continue being for the next fifteen, but most of us play because it's fun, it affords gentle exercise, the company is congenial, the beer has a good head to it, and we can pretend for a brief period that this time our latent skills will blossom and give us that control over events which is so obviously absent from our normal lives.

Even the Great Ones, they who dominate their destinies decisively, and whose mental powers are far beyond those possessed or even postulated as necessary by the sporting savants, play for escape, not continuity. I play for an occasional side one of whose occasional members is a most learned Professor of Theology, a man with a mind as sharp as the pins on which he makes angels dance, and who is also an able administrator and a loved and respected pastor. He is one of those once-quickish bowlers who nowadays demands respect but who perhaps does not pose problems to openers as frequently as he did. He tends to bowl a few overs of fairly harmless accurate stuff, and then, just when his captain is thinking of polite ways of asking him to give way to younger blood, and the batsmen are beginning to open out, a bit of the old magic comes back, he moves a few sharply in off a good length, takes two quick wickets, then takes himself off. He revels in his cricket, but not because it poses profound problems; he gets enough of them in his daily routine. Partly it is because it allows him to be a little boy again, but note the qualification of his final act. That, more than anything else, explains why, if a manager says 'The Prof is turning out,' men will motor many miles for such a match, for they know that his presence guarantees it will be played in the proper spirit. He has, you see, the one quality which marks the true cricketer, one which he shares with others much less well endowed with wits, of varying fortunes, from every class and of all conditions and capabilities.

He is a gentleman.

But even cricketers like to flex their minds occasionally as well as their muscles, and if you feel like doing so now, here is a puzzle with a cricketing flavour. It has nothing to do with the game in reality – the playing of the game poses no problems of this sort – but a good knowledge of its ins and outs is required to reach a solution.

It is not new; it was set originally by Sir Arthur Eddington, Professor of Astronomy at Cambridge before the Second World War, and resurrected by Fred Hoyle, who held the Chair in the immediate post-war years, in his book *The Nature of the Universe*, published in 1950.

Its solution requires no mathematics beyond the most elementary. Each stage is a step in simple logic which any cricketer should be able to take. To answer the question set, you will have to work out precisely what happened in every over bowled; it doesn't look as if you are given enough information to do so, but you are.

Readers of the younger generation may be intrigued by the way in which the players' names are printed: this is not arbitrary. Eddington set the problem in 1938, and in those days these subtle differences implied distinctions which were rigidly enforced. For further information consult one of your elders and betters.

Here it is; good luck!

Extract from the score of a cricket match between Eastshire and Westshire

EASTSHIRE – SECOND INNINGS

A. A. Atkins	6
Bodkins	8
D. D. Dawkins	6
Hawkins	6
Jenkins (J.)	5
Larkins	4
Meakins	7
Hon. P. P. Perkins	11
Capt. S. S. Simkins	6
Tomkins	0
Wilkins	1
Extras	0
	—
Total	60
	—

Bowling

	Overs	Mdns	Runs	Wkts
Pitchwell	12.1	2	14	8
Speedwell	6	0	15	1
Tosswell	7	5	31	1

The score was composed entirely of singles and fours. There were no catches, no-balls, or short runs.

Speedwell and Tosswell each had only one spell of bowling. Pitchwell bowled the first over, Mr Atkins taking first ball. Speedwell was the other opening bowler.

[95]

Whose wickets were taken by Speedwell and Tosswell?
Who was not out?
What was the score at the fall of each wicket?

I'm sure you'll be able to work it out without help from me, but if you need a hand to explain to your infant son how you reached your intuitive solution write to me (c/o Willow Books, 8 Grafton Street, London W1) and I will send you an outline of the steps involved.

Computer Cricket

HE WAS OUT; of that I have no doubt.

Debate after the match hinged on the fact that he had waltzed four paces down the wicket before the ball struck his pads; slight notice was taken of the tangential impertinence offered by a mere spectator, that it seemed to him that decision came fractionally before appeal.

I held that I, as umpire, was in the best position to judge all the relevant factors, such as that the ball probably would, or even might, have struck the wicket; that it was a terrible shot anyway; and that he was the loutish fellow who had protested so audibly over a not-out verdict of mine in the previous innings. The point raised by some of his team-mates, that I was at square leg at the time, was a nicety to which I gave little weight. I am now inclined to admit that I was influenced a shade too much by my assessment of him as a thoroughly unpleasant piece of work, but it will be a sad day when character and personality cease to be active in determining the outcome of sporting events, and especially cricket. It is unfortunately true that in business, politics, and even some games, Good Guys tend to come second, but it is not yet generally the case in cricket, and whenever I am umpiring I try to do my little bit to ensure that virtue, good manners, and gentlemanly decorum count for something in the score-book as well as in the general estimation.

Invitations to stand have been falling off recently; I shall have to change club again. The little altercation in the pavilion has set me thinking about two things (well, four to be exact, but I have paid the fine, and the crown on my tooth hardly shows at all): really unpleasant people I have known, and the influence of personality in cricket.

In an odd way the two apparently disparate issues fuse in the person of a man I met again recently after a gap of over thirty years. Until I saw him I had not realized how much I had enjoyed missing him. He can stand as an epitome of what I want to say on these topics, especially as, in my younger days, when the tiny canvas of my knowledge had not been smudged by the realization of its inadequacy, I thought the term was a classical circumlocution for a belch.

Stinkie MacFlannel was, without doubt, the most unpleasant and unsuccessful boy I knew in all my days at school, and I recall that one of the nice things about leaving was the thought that I would never have to have anything to do with Stinkie again, ever, in any circumstances, at all, anywhere, to my dying day, and not even thereafter if I lived a moderately good life.

I found myself sitting next to him the other evening at the sort of City dinner I get invited to by mistake. I must admit that since I last saw him thirty-five years ago, he has changed considerably; he still has horrendous halitosis, a scrofulous complexion, inherent bad manners, a cerebellar incoherence which spreads physical devastation in his wake, and a body odour which would put him at risk if he ever got upwind of a Brahmin bull. Nowadays, however, he is also totally bald, paunchy, and highly successful in the sense that he is flush with money, greatly influential in High Places, and married to a famous beauty whom age has not withered nor custom staled.

My envy, while following the rise and rise of Sir Hector MacFlannel, has been shaded a less virulent green by the knowledge that the only pleasure he gets out of his money is much the same as that a pig gets from its straw – the joy of rolling in it. I dismiss the Power he wields with the thought that in any Corridor Stinkie happens to be walking I am very happy not to be; and any sexual jealousy I may have felt when I saw press photographs of the happy couple at his smart society wedding died a rapid death when I met his bride soon afterwards, and realized that her looks would indeed be unaffected by time, but largely due to the durable properties of silicone, foam rubber, and the sort of patina applied equally to the faces of the professionally glamorous and the façades of pebble-dashed suburbia.

Stinkie was, and is, one of those unfortunates who can do nothing right. He couldn't kick a ball, he couldn't hold a bat. He had perfect vision, but he didn't seem to be looking at the same world as the rest of us; at least, it seemed to be a different shape. He preferred magarine to butter – and this was the margarine of 1944, which tasted as if a large bird had produced it rather than, as later, given it a name – but apart from that had no apparent preferences in food, which is not surprising, because very little of it stayed in his mouth long enough for his tongue to have registered that it was there. His table-manners were disgusting, and for young boys to have noticed them they must have been remarkable indeed.

He was useless in class; children don't usually hold that against their fellows, but Stinkie was obtrusively bad in a way that irritated the masters. Such irritation always rubs off on the innocent, and contrary to the image of classroom life propagated by the comic papers, the happy schoolboy is the one who has combined with his fellows to induce a state of euphoric docility in his Dominie. A highly experienced form can, with careful control, create ecstatic inertia in a room dedicated to the busy stuffing of resistant juvenile grey-matter. A child like Stinkie acts as a grain of sand, producing perils rather than pearls, and other children quickly learn to shun him and, whenever possible, shut him up.

Of course, it was not Stinkie's fault that he was a walking disaster area, that his genetic inheritance had moulded him to fit

[99]

an existence radically different from ours. To an adult, the rejection by children of certain of the misfits among them seems cruel, but it should be noted that the young never attack square pegs merely because they are square, nor do they insist forcibly that they smooth off their corners, unless they hurt those they rub against. They do, however, get very angry if those few pegs try to square off all the holes in the world. If this seems counter to modern enlightened educational and sociological theory, it must stand as a comment on the children or the theory.

For my part, I side with the children. The Good Book tells us to love our enemies, which to me means anyone who threatens my survival or my way of life, such as the batsman at the other end who hits the ball firmly to cover point's right hand and calls me for a quick single. Nowhere, as far as I can see, are we ordered to like them, or encourage them, or not send them back when they are two-thirds of the way down the wicket.

I therefore record it as a not-very-surprising fact, and not as a heart-rending excuse for all subsequent social maladjustment, that Hector MacFlannel grew up with a powerful distaste for his fellow men. He erected powerful barriers against their interference in his affairs, and tried whenever possible to eliminate consideration of them from his interests and endeavours.

It is significant that his one great passion was for numbers; he loved them for their inhumanity, and he played with them as other children play with toys. He had no interest in what the numbers might mean, or in the great abstractions underlying them, for he was in no sense a mathematician. It was this interest that led him to pay attention to cricket, for he was attracted by any activity which generated numbers. Railways fascinated him also, and perhaps brought even more satisfaction, for what set of figures bears less connection to reality and causes more human frustration than a British railway timetable? He would spend hours poring over trains and Tests, Bradshaw and Bradman, with complete lack of discrimination.

Of course, there are figures and figures. Two other of my school contemporaries got into trouble handling them over-enthusiastically. Slippy Sleeman graduated from pocket money peculation, which got him expelled, to fraudulent conversion on a massive scale, which is considered legal and laudable and has taken him to a respected position in the financial world. Randy Miller, on the other hand (and a mutual female friend once said that the trouble with Randy was that he always seemed to have another hand), moved on from studying the Theory of Forms in the glossy pages of *Men Only* tucked into a school atlas, to advanced practice in most of the holiday resorts along the South Coast. The judge remarked that his downfall could be ascribed ironically to lack of attention to the key figures 1 and 16, these being respectively the number of wives you are allowed concurrently, and the age of consent.

I would not like it to be thought that I find anything reprehensible in the collection of cricketing statistics. Collecting anything can be great fun, and it is a natural fledgling way of expressing enthusiasm or devotion – when I discovered, on my fifteenth birthday, that Doris Day was already married, I burned 283 photographs in a frenzy of shattered hopes. It can also tell you much about the game, and the collector. An Australian student friend once told me how he saw his intellectual status slump in the faces round a High Table, and realized his words were wafting his hoped-for fellowship out of the window when he answered a casual question on the latest Test score by saying '3 for 92'.

Stinkie's interest in numbers led him, when he left school, to take up computer programming. It seems strange now that an obvious twit like Hector MacFlannel could get involved in such a high-powered field, but it must be remembered that those were early days in computers, and any farmer will tell you that a field fresh to the plough will nourish rank weeds as well as productive plants. Look at the primal period of any new technology and you find a heady mix of idiocy and genius, with those not directly involved having trouble sorting out which is which. If you doubt me, think of automobiles and aviation not long ago, electronics recently, sociology now, politics always.

Our hero boned up on BASIC and wrote his first programme; cricket comes into the story again, for he chose to try out his new skills by creating a system whereby people and their undesirable vagaries could be completely eliminated from the game. The programme was designed to prime the computer with the Laws, the current statistics of all the County players (and in those days, Gentlemen also), the past records of the wickets at the leading grounds, the possible effects of the weather, the known prejudices of the first-class Panel, and every detail from *Wisden* down to the last footnote. As can be imagined, it took much sweat, much midnight oil, and two and a half years. When it was complete, all that had to be done at the start of a season was to feed in the names of the members of the County teams and the fixture list, press the button, and the machine printed out the detailed score-sheets of every match in fifteen minutes flat.

He managed to borrow the α-Integrated Reflux Thingummy at Harwell for the trial run. This was difficult, for in those days computers were rare and precious things, and only organizations vital to the Welfare of Mankind were allowed to have them: places such as Aldermaston, Porton Down, and the Pools Promotion Research Unit. He achieved this breakthrough by breaking in; this was long before the present free-and-easy system was set up, by which, as I understand it, anyone can summon up the total cooperation of any computer by dialling the correct telephone number and feeding in the binary equivalent of abracadabra.

It was a complete disaster, for two fundamental reasons. Even had the programmer been of the highest innovative capability, he could never in a hundred years have reduced to figures and symbols the endless variety and subtlety of a game like cricket – it is the very vagaries of the players that pattern it, the eccentricities of the environment that express it, the unpredictable that predicates it. In other words, a computer has to know, and in cricket you never do.

The other reason was the one stated earlier: Stinkie was no good at this either. The programme was as full of faults as San Andreas, and the print-out looked like a seismographical survey of the region *circa* 18 April 1906.

His prospective career in ruins, Stinkie sank deep into despair. He cursed his fate for not endowing him more, his parents for not loving him more, his school for not teaching him more, and the Inspector of Taxes for choosing that moment to demand the instant supply of precise details of his financial affairs. He was distraught and confused, and out of his confusion his success was born, which is just as well, for his mind in a clear state was about as seminal as a rampant heraldic lion – all ancient flashy show but no action.

In a muddled fury, he stuffed the documents in the envelope pre-addressed to the Inland Revenue Commissioners, and posted it off. He got that wrong too – it was the cricket computer programme.

Her Majesty's Lords Commissioners were at that time considering plans for the total computerization of the entire taxation system, and when Stinkie's programme reached them they assumed it was a contender for the software contract. It was sent for expert analysis; their consultant assessor happened to be one of the rare geniuses in the field, and even rarer in having a sense of humour. His report ended; 'This programme is the product either of a brilliant twisted mind, or a total incompetent. If put into practice it would establish an array of levies without any logical basis, completely arbitrary in action, lacking the rigidity of reason and the flexibility of compassion. It would be monumentally unfair, but has one overriding characteristic which I recommend to your Lordships' consideration – nobody would be able to understand it sufficiently enough to mount a coherent appeal against it.'

This report was instantly recognized as a description of the ideal taxation system (from the Treasury point of view), and voted through on the nod, *nem. con.* To justify its adoption, its author was lauded as a luminary, loaded with further contracts from other departments, and heaped with handsome fees and fine dignities.

He never found it necessary to write another programme, so if you find that tomorrow's post has brought you a tax demand greater than your total income, or a telephone bill for frequent trunk calls to Kathmandu, or a massive gas account printed in red when you went all-electric twelve years ago, or even if the letter should have been delivered to someone on the other side of town – don't get all upset.

Just remember that you're really only playing cricket the Stinkie MacFlannel way.

Paternal Cricket

I HAVE NEVER FOUND the notion of reincarnation much of a comfort. If I fail to get Life sorted out satisfactorily this time round, I cannot see how relegation to the Fourth or Fifth Division for a second season is going to help. I have yet to meet a single frog or spider who seemed remotely qualified, or likely to become so, for the task of disentangling distorted personal relationships on an inter-human level, much less higher. Nor is it obvious to me how a short stretch in an Amphibian or Arachnid arena would fit me more fully to battle better on the people plane.

Nonetheless, the experience of *déjà vu* is a common one, and most of us have our tale to tell of having been there before. Mine is unusual in that it is only recently I realized I had one. My son was looking through his old school photographs with that long-range nostalgia which the young do so well, and he handed one across to me with the comment: 'That was what I once thought was the greatest cricket match I ever played in.'

It was the group photograph of his prep school 1st XI Fathers' Match, and there we both were, he much smaller, I much wider, he with much less hair, I with much more. There were Chris and Alec, Bob, Toby and Charles, Slippy, Twizzle and Tiny (wasn't he enormous, even at that age?). There were Chris's Dad, and Alec's, and Toby's Uncle Jim, and that funny little man who claimed to be Slippy Peel's father, and turned out to be his Mum's latest temporary.

There also were Brush Harris and Washer Nutt, the art master and cricket coach, co-opted to replace Terence O'Flaherty's father and much older brother, who were absent due to the pressing claims of a pair of monumental hangovers diligently developed the night before at a highly successful wake. Toby's Uncle Jim thought it 'a pretty poor show, don't yer know, them not appearin' on parade, what, what?' (he had done his National Service as a Lance Corporal in the Catering Corps). 'Never caught me missin' a show like that.' To do him justice, he had indeed measured up to the same problem with complete success every morning for the last fifteen years, though it was now taking rather more measures than it used to.

We wallowed in the nostalgia for a while, an indulgent habit young people pick up carelessly because it pleasures them casually, like good sherry, and the old are hooked on intemperately, because it gives them the comfort in their second infancy that thumb-sucking gave them in their first.

Then the talk moved into the 'Where is So-and-so now?' stage, and of this I am not so fond as I was. I am reaching the age when each celebration of a new step taken by the younger generation along the avenue of life reminds me more forcibly that I am, as the racing drivers say, rapidly running out of road. My father warned me that middle age is first signalled when the policemen start looking young. What does it signify, I ask myself, when the mothers at my pupils' Parents' Evenings start looking pretty? Or when my daughter's toothsome mini-skirted friends are overheard describing me as 'sweet'?

Sweet, indeed! Did Minnie Baverstock, blond bombshell of

the North-Eastern Institute of Domestic Science and Associated Cultural Studies, Miss Inter-Collegiate of 1952, call me sweet? Well, actually she did, but ask anyone what happened to her. All the same I still say she shouldn't have married him, no matter what the Warden said.

I sat looking down at the faces of those two teams of not-so-long-ago; my eyes gazed, then glazed, and I found my focus fading through the shining surface of that pair of generations to the depth of the overlapping previous pair. I saw two other teams, another place, clothes slightly odd, stances strangely stilted, but the same game, the same ages, and one person the same – myself.

It came to me that I had played in two such matches: the first against my father, the second against my son. My abstract stare accommodated a clearing vision of that earlier event, and I lived again what had been for me also, the greatest match ever . . .

We had a super team that year; we won nearly all our matches . . . Well, to be strict with memory and word-sequence, we nearly won all our matches. Our cricket-master, old 'Screw' Driver, said we were the best bowling side he had ever coached at St Timothy's, and the fact that we skittled out successive opponent teams for scores of 21, 15, 30, 27, 18, and even, in the last School match of the season, a memorable 9, supports his contention. The qualifying fact that they then skittled us out for matching scores of 18, 11, 25, 22, 14, and even, in the last School match of the season, a haunting 4, suggests either that their coaches also had the best bowling sides they had ever had, or we couldn't bat for peanuts.

I suspect the latter theory has more of the truth in it. Jimmy Elliott and Harry Mandeville went on to take a lot of wickets in League cricket (in East Fife and Mombasa respectively), but none of us ever made any runs really, not even our most illustrious O.B., Gordon Cuddlesome, who went on to a Blue and the fringes of County cricket by the ruthless employment of a rigidly self-centred defensive technique, sustained interminably on an unshakable belief in his own ability, which combined with an obtrusive modesty to convince everyone that, since he spent an awful long time out there, he must be doing something of value. He later applied the same technique when his impressive sporting credentials hoisted him into a series of senior and responsible executive posts at the very heart of industry, eventually earning the title bestowed on him (by a bankrupted shareholder with medical training) of 'The Infarct that Winded the Economic Body of Britain'.

So we came to this, the final match of our prep school ist XI careers, the climax of the end of term Old Boys Week, determined to snatch Victory from the Jaws of Despair. That, at least, is how old Screwy put it, as the keynote slogan energizing his pep-talk after fielding practice the night before, although most of us reckoned that the elusive morsel had slipped much further down the beast's alimentary tract by this stage in the season, and trying to drag it back up could be a bit unproductive.

It looked a formidable side that the HM had lined up against us. I had played some pretty serious and hairy cricket opposite some of them in back gardens from here to Ewel East, and had in particular faced up to the elder Mandeville's away-swinging Chinaman on a pitch where reading his action was made tricky by the curly casts of those wiggly worms you dig up to use as bait for mackerel, to use as bait for conger, to use as bait for lobsters, which used to make me come out in spots and throw up all over.

We expected Squiffy MacFarlane's Dad to pose problems, too, for it was well known that he had in his youth opened the attack for one of the English County sides. As a boy one should be a bit careful about accepting the claims one's fellows make for the prowess of their parents – the Selfish Gene flexes its egoistic vocal cords at a tender age – but this one was authentic. It did not, in the event, deliver the threat it augured for several reasons: Squiffy turned out to represent a very late upsurge on the MacFarlane virility chart; Dad was positively geriatric; the County was Rutland; and the side the Reserve 'B' (Touring).

Our two youngest members of staff were due to play, and no doubt they would have been useful, for both had been 'active in the sporting life of their Training Establishment', as the head master had put it in his Welcoming Words at the beginning of term. He had been somewhat vague over where that had been, and so had they, but it must have been Government sponsored, for Eustace had crowns stamped all over his pads; and it must have been the same for both, for he and Jeremy ('Christian names, please, my dears; we hope to be ever-so-open in our relationships.') were obviously very, very close friends. Unfortunately, they never turned up, due in some obscure way to their attendance at the Old Boys' annual wine and cheese party the night before. Bobby Eldridge heard Screwy Driver going on about 'not knowing when you've had your fill', and we sympathized, remembering how ill we had felt the morning after eating whole packs of scrumptious chocolate marshmallows during a dorm feast. We expected it had been something like that.

We lost the toss, and they put us in, which surprised and puzzled us, since just before the coin was spun, Screwy reminded our captain forcefully of the maxim that 'the side that elects to bat controls the match'. Nor was he now a disinterested spectator, for he had been subbed in to play for the fathers, and he was drawn into urgent consultation with their skipper before the decision was announced.

We were pleased that Mr Driver was to play; we liked him, we respected him, he was fun to be with, and he taught us a lot about cricket. Nowadays no self-respecting headmaster would risk employing such a man to run the cricket in his school, for he was what would, in the present confident professional educationalist-dominated system, be dismissed as an absurdity, a hopeless performer who was an excellent teacher. When taxed with this apparent contradiction, old Screwy (who had a touch of the holies in his spare time) would point out that, if you want training in how to succeed as a saint, it is better to seek out a sinner, for the saints produce their perfect performances without having to think how, but the sinners know only too well what they ought to have done, and what they ought not to have done, and the repentant ones have analysed the problems with often obsessive care.

We batted jolly well – everyone said so – and knocked up the respectable total of 86. Mind you, we were aided by some very loose bowling and appalling slack fielding. I have never seen a set of fingers so singularly and collectively oleaginous. Catches went down like cream-puffs at a Mothers' Guild meeting, and over half our score was in byes. If we had produced such a weedy performance, it would have been Coventry from the House and no jam for tea from the housemaster.

As batsmen, the fathers all showed symptoms of Athletic Amnesia, moving their limbs as if they knew all the correct positions but had forgotten the precise sequence. As a result, they tended to make a few runs then get out just as they looked set for a decent score. It was surprising how many went, fatally agricultural, immediately after a word of encouragement from their captain.

This was true of all but the Rev. Joshua Cleek, Sam's Dad. He was a huge man, strong in the Lord and a few other places as well, for Sam was one of twelve, at least. He delivered long sermons to his flock on Sundays, and long irons to the pin most of the rest of the week. His handicap had come down year by year in exact inverse proportion to the number of his offspring, and it was well known he had his eye on the club Scratch Medal, which worried his wife and his bishop for similar reasons, based on the reputation he was developing in the trade as the only man who had managed to convert the charities for the children of the clergy into a cottage industry, and the fact that he began his golfing career also as a rabbit.

He was obviously no cricketer, but his single repeated response to every ball received was in character with his answer to all the problems presented to him by his ministry – he charged head on, and smote them hip and thigh, hip being in this case high over the square leg boundary, and thigh full-toss into the tennis courts.

With half an hour to go, it looked as if they had the game stitched up; 81 for 6, Joshua Creek 49 not out. Then his partner missed a straight full-toss, and my father headed for the wicket. At that moment my pride in him was near to bursting, and my only worry was that his flannels were in much the same state. Halfway to the wicket he was recalled for an urgent and serious consultation with his skipper; he tossed his hair – well, perhaps tossed is rather a strong verb for what he was able to do – gave a grim laugh, and strode on with fell purpose in his stride. Here, I thought, comes the *coup de grâce*; a few decisive blows, and all is over, nobly determined. Enough of this toying with children; here is reality.

There were indeed only a few blows, and one in particular was decisive. Dad took strike, tickled it down to fine leg rather neatly, and called the Reverend Joshua for an easy single. As they passed in mid-run, I was almost sure – but I must have muddled what I thought I saw – that my father slipped his bat between the scissoring shins of the pounding padre. Whatever the cause, down he went in a temple-shaking tumble, from which he did not recover in time to avoid being run out. He was applauded to the pavilion by his team-mates with what seemed to me excessively cheerful enthusiasm. 81 for 7.

As was the custom, I was called up to bowl the next over at my father. Now, I knew my Dad's strengths and weaknesses with the bat from many hours of intense two-man matches up and down the covered way that linked his surgery with the dental laboratory next door. One wall of the corridor, that on a batsman's off-side the way we played, was solid brick, but the other was glass from about knee-height, and this severely inhibited the leg-side stroke play of a full-grown man. As a result, my father was a sucker for a fast, straight, full-pitch aimed at the base of his leg stump. I fizzed just such a delivery down at him first ball, and he hit it past me so hard I hadn't moved when I heard it rattle against the fence. I had forgotten the special rule for such matches – the Dads bat left-handed. 85 for 7. Surprisingly the rest of his side showed little enthusiasm for this quantum-leap towards victory, and my father looked more guilty than pleased. The next ball was the one I bring out of the back of my hand, but unfortunately I brought it out a bit late, and it bounced four times before he dollied it delicately back into my grateful grasp.

The score was 85 for 8, and the last two wickets fell without further resistance, so we had won; but if at first we could not comprehend that it had happened, later we could not comprehend how. Nevertheless it was a win, our first, and our cups were very soon full and running over with joy and the very dilute orange squash St Timothy's lashed out with on those festive occasions.

The longer memory dimmed, and the closer contest cleared again . . .

I am told that the trouble with bull-fighting is that the whole thing is a fix; the bull is going to lose, no matter what, and everyone knows it. Except the bull, of course, and nobody tells it, otherwise it might not want to play. Since the outcome is pre-determined, and all but one of the participants, and all the spectators, are in on the secret, the whole point of the exercise shifts over to the ritual, the way in which the customary climax is contrived. Woe betide anyone even remotely involved if the result is reversed, the liturgy tainted. Managements resign, riots break out, governments fall, sometimes a man dies. The bull gets killed anyway; it might give the younger generation ideas.

In an inverted, left-handed sort of way, the same is true of Fathers' Matches, seen from the adult side. The boys always win; everyone knows that, except the boys, and tradition makes mandatory the appearance of a close finish. Given the wide range in the level of fitness, ability, and habitual sobriety of the average set of fathers, this is not always an easy thing to arrange, but failure brings dire consequences, collective and individual. Lysistrata's strategy was libidinous compared with that of a preppy mother cheated of her child's victory. Schools have been switched by an outraged Inspectorate from 'Recognized' to 'Approved'. A certain well-known politician failed in his ambition to reach Number 10 because the word was passed that he once played in a winning Fathers' side.

We won the toss, and put them in; it is important to know how many you're not meant to get. It turned out to be 94, just about right, though it took a bit of luck to get them there, plus an inspired late no-ball call from Toby's Grandad (very supportive, Toby's family) at square-leg umpire.

Our innings started off well; we lost wickets steadily but not too obviously, and the score mounted with satisfactory sluggishness. Then Slippy Peel's Mum's latest lost his head. He hit two fours off successive balls from his pseudo-son, and was instantly carried away by the cricketers' equivalent of Motorway Madness. Power-crazy, he started thrashing the ball to the four corners of the tiny ground, endangering little lives and limbs, as well as our great desire to do the decent thing.

Then his partner lost his off stump, and I was heading for the crease. My captain called me back for a moment; I listened carefully, nodded my agreement to his wise words, and went on. The first ball was a gentle long hop, and I cuffed it gently past the umpire, calling instantly for what seemed an easy run, or maybe two.

It was not until he was well on his way down the wicket that the high-scoring Lothario saw what I and my skipper should have noticed as I walked out – Slippy was lurking with intent just behind square leg, almost completely camouflaged by the long white coat umpires wore in those days. Not best pleased by his treatment when bowling, he hurled the ball in with deadly accuracy, clipping off a bail on the fifth bounce.

That was, in effect, the end of our innings; token resistance was offered, but our wickets fell more or less on schedule, and our honour was upheld in the adult world, even if our cricketing reputations were jeopardized in the juvenile.

And what was the deep slice of Sporting Philosophy passed on to me by my glorious leader as I went out to make my little contribution to our Noble Game? It was short and sharp: 'For God's sake run the idiot out, or we might win this b. . . . . match!'

Pavilion Cricket

IT IS WELL KNOWN that the most profound cultural advances, both in the arts and technology, are often the result of accidental stumbling rather than deliberate forward steps. The modern concept of 'spin-off' is a more polite way of putting it, but nonetheless implies that the officially directed research is rotational, getting nowhere fast, while the valuable products are those that fly off at a tangent. This is an overstatement of a doubtful case, but I can give you three examples of deep social significance.

In 1892 Sir James Dewar managed to cool air to a temperature of about $-200°$ Centigrade, at which level it is a liquid. To keep it in that state, he designed a special double-walled bottle, made of silvered glass, with the air evacuated from the space between the walls. He saw no possible practical use for the bottle, other than that for which he had designed it, and did not even bother to take a patent out on it, but what would watching cricket be like, for those without access to the pavilion, without a hot cuppa from a Thermos flask in the tea interval?

My second example is from the world of the arts, or at least a petty though glittering satellite. In the 1930s the manager of an obscure American canning factory made a bad miscalculation, and the company found itself stuck with a warehouse full of tins of spinach. I have heard that people who tasted the contents at the time suspected that it was really seaweed; this is unfair – all tinned spinach tastes like seaweed. Be that as it may, they were left with the problem of trying to unload the revolting stuff on to the paying public, and resorted to the usual way of persuading people to purchase products they neither want nor need – advertising. The selling pitch did not work, the company went burst (as did the cans years later in a derelict warehouse in Smalltown, USA), but the character created to plug the product on film developed a life of his own, and has given more healthful happiness to countless children of all ages than would the contents of the cans he consumes to give him his miraculous muscles. He was, of course, Popeye the Sailor Man.

Thus, of my two examples so far, the first started in low temperature physics and ended in picnic baskets, while the second began in food industry marketing and wound up on children's television. My third began in economics and high finance, and turns out, surprisingly, to have some bearing on cricket. Let me explain . . .

Golf has been described as a pleasant walk ruined by occasional bouts of violent exercise; cricket can be characterized as a boring occupation redeemed by the fact that during matches most players spend most of their time not playing it. Thus the former is a reflection in sport of the working life of the rural population of the glens and highlands of Scotland, while the latter does the same for the urban equivalent in the factories and offices of England.

The pleasantly spasmodic nature of our national Summer Sport is partly due to the fact that we don't really have one – a Summer, that is. A South American friend once sat with me through the damp and dreary afternoon of a Lord's Test, and informed me at the end that in his opinion we don't have a sport either, but he was used to sultry sessions in burning bullrings killing Castilian cattle, and he found the glacial slaughter of an Indian middle order on a green sticky less than exciting.

It is one of the glorious absurdities of cricket that the basic uniform is of light material, white to reflect the heat of a blazing sun which is seldom present, and loose to allow evaporation of the sweat which is rarely produced. It is then enveloped in numerous heavy-knit woollen sweaters, totally cancelling the original conception, which it must be admitted leant towards laxity and favoured frivolity, neither of which have any place in a game.

To cricketers, a temperate climate means tempering enthusiasm with patience; in this country, a great deal of the summer is spent sitting around in pavilions waiting for the rain to stop. This suits the temperaments of players and spectators admirably, for if there is one thing the people of this country love more than playing games or watching them, it is talking about them. This is not so much a society of shopkeepers as a nation of natterers. Go into any shop here, any proper shop (not one of those transatlantic monstrosities with miles of shelves guarded by rows of till-gates): you will find that the staff are more concerned with conversation than commerce, and would much rather retail gossip than groceries.

So it is with cricket. To the *cognoscenti*, BBC radio coverage of Test matches is much preferred over television. Why? Because of the talk, the chatter, the tales, the tittletattle – very little of it about the game actually in progress. I am reliably informed by a cousin who knows almost nothing about these things that the listening figures go up whenever the game is interrupted – during the lunch interval, or when rain has stopped play. This may be due to all those who have been tuned to television turning over because there is nothing left to watch, but I suspect it is because listeners know that the broadcasting team will no longer be distracted by action from the really important business of conversation.

Watch that row of players and their friends sitting in the deckchairs in front of the pavilion at any cricket match below first-class County level. They are not really paying any attention to the game, though some are padded up and waiting to go in to bat. They are deep in the most diverting discussions, and when one of them is forced by the fall of a wicket to leave the group and head out towards the middle, he does so with evident reluctance, continuing the causerie as long as he can, and often returning to it within minutes, with obvious relief at not having missed too many of the *bons-mots*.

The palaver-pattern is built into the very structure of the game. As each ball is bowled, the fielders move in towards the centre of the field; this brings each player close enough to his immediate neighbours for a quick word or two. After every six balls, the entire team converges on the middle for a brief chat about this and that. (In Australia, where they have a more limited vocabulary, they have an eight-ball over.) Roughly every six overs, the captain changes the bowling. This is theoretically a tactical exercise but, given the bowlers that the average skipper has for these permutations, the change itself is relatively unimportant. Its value is in morale; not in the sense that the prospect of the new bowler gives the rest of the team a surge of fresh hope – they know very well he is just as bad as the one he is replacing – but because the time involved in the process of adjusting the field (otherwise pointless, for how can you change a placing pattern to compensate for a switch from Right-Arm-Over-Fast-Inaccurate-Slinger to Left-Arm-Round-Slow-Incompetent-Chucker?) allows that much longer for team discussion groups to form, mingle, and pass a bit more than the tantalizing time-of-day titbits possible in the normal over-changes.

Then there are the Lunch Intervals. These are completely misnamed nowadays, the term dating from the days when a cold collation would be laid out at the edge of the meadow by the Gentlemen's gentlemen, who had travelled down on top of the postillion. Since commercial catering firms took over, no one has been known actually to eat the plastic meals provided in pavilions. Most of the forty minutes allowed is taken up in a combination of lingual busyness and beery lubrication. What happens in the rest is one of the most closely guarded secrets of the cricketing brotherhood; were I to reveal it, I would be drummed out of the game forever, and forced to turn in my Litesome. Suffice it to say that mixed matches, though tolerated these days in a generous spirit of sexual equality approximating towards athletic idiocy, are never started before 2.30 p.m.; some things are still sacred.

But to return to the weather, which is something the English do with as much insistence as the French do to sex – could it be that each suffers from a surfeit, that the obsessions are in fact oblique objections? – the point is that conversation must be accompanied by an unimportant untaxing activity, such as listening to light music, or taking tea, or watching serious television programmes. When play is stopped by bad weather for a lengthy period, cricketers turn to other diversions as a background for their badinage. Pavilion Cricket is one such diversion.

Pavilion Cricket is played by drawing up two teams in the usual way – real, mythical, flattering, or libellous – and then employing some convenient random-chance method of ascribing a score to them. Perhaps the best way is that of rolling specially manufactured dice. These come in various forms; the type with which I am most familiar is a pair of little brass cylinders, one slightly larger than the other. Both are hexagonal in cross-section, so that when rolled along a flat surface, they will come to rest with one of the faces uppermost. On the larger of the two cylinders, five of the faces are inscribed respectively with the numbers 1, 2, 3, 4, and 6, with a question mark on the last (or the word HOWZAT, and I have a feeling one variety used to be sold under that name). The other smaller cylinder has on its faces the words or letters BOWLED, CAUGHT, STUMPED, LBW, RUN OUT, and NOT OUT.

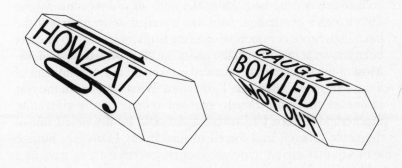

The first man to face up (or his captain acting on his behalf), rolls the batting die: if a number shows up on top, that is his score for the delivery. If the question mark (or HOWZAT) shows, the bowler (or his captain) rolls the other die, and the batsman's fate is decided on the turn of that cylinder. If one of the fatal words turns up, he goes, and his place is taken by the next man in; if NOT OUT, he lives to roll again.

So the game goes on, and it is a good game too, but in recent years I have found it difficult to find the little brass dice I have described. It is possible to make a Do-it-Yourself substitute, but until recently these had usually proved unsatisfactory, because of the difficulty of ensuring that the randomness of the chance was not totally destroyed by the irregularity of their construction. The usual way was to draw rough circles on paper, cut them out, and construct little spinning-tops from them with matchsticks. There are two serious sources of error in this:

1. Very few of us can draw perfect circles freehand.
2. Even if this is overcome by tracing the outline of a coin (the old half-crown was about the right size), it is impossible easily to divide a circle into equal segments without proper instruments.

This is where my third example of a major social advance appearing as spin-off comes in, the one involving economics and high finance. In 1971 the pound was decimalised: Someone in Authority had at last noticed that we have ten fingers.

The switch destroyed the meaning of shillings and six-pences, florins and half-crowns, and so required the introduction of a new coinage, which duly appeared. There was much debate about these new coins, some of it heated, and without doubt the most controversial was the 50p piece. Most of the dissension arose over its shape, which is seven-sided, but with curved sides. We are used to it now, but at the time of its introduction it was new and unfamiliar, which was probably the main reason for its initial unpopularity; that is understandable and excusable.

The coin has, however, one enormous asset: it forms a perfect template for the construction of a simple but accurate set of dice for Pavilion Cricket, easily made in the most humble of pavilions. All else that is needed is a pencil or pen, a straight edge, and a source of cardboard (preferably white). These should all be readily available, for if it is raining, the scorer won't need his pencil, and the score-book provides the edge. Cigarette packs can yield suitable cardboard (British only – continental and American brands are flabby and lacking in fibre); or, at matches where programmes are on sale, these are useful for this if for nothing else.

Full instructions are provided below for the construction of such a DIY Pavilion Cricket set, and I wish you many happy hours playing with it. One word of warning – be as careful in your choice of opponent as you would be for a friendly cricket match of the real sort – it is possible to cheat. If you do find yourself matched unwillingly against persons of doubtful probity, watch out for the off-centre matchstick and the over-clipped arc; get very suspicious if you start losing after he stops chewing, and re-member that the unilateral application of sweat, spit, or shellac can influence the spin of a die as easily as it does the swing of a ball.

PAVILION CRICKET
DIY cut out kit instructions

I.   Lay 50p piece flat on cardboard; run pencil round edge to form outline.

II. Return 50p piece to owner; draw small circle in centre of figure. (This is fairly easy to judge, but if it bothers you, drop perpendiculars from three of the angles to the middles of the opposite sides, on the reverse; where they cross is the centre.)

III. Draw a line from each of the angles in to the centre, thus dividing the figure up like a cake into seven equal segments. Repeat all this to give you two figures. (You'll have to borrow the 50p again – ask nicely.)

IV. Fill in the letters and numbers as shown in the diagrams. (Note: this is the Full Match Mode – if you want a quick fifteen-over thrash-around, substitute a question mark for one of the ones, and a run out for one of the not outs.)

V. Cut the figures out, then trim the edges in straight lines from each angle to the next.

VI. Drill a small hole through the circle (the point of the pencil will do it nicely), then push a matchstick through until the disc of cardboard is about ¼ of the way up from the (unused) head. Now take it off and put it back on with the letters/numbers on the upper surface. Repeat for the other disc, and you've made it. Well done! In my next book, how to make your own nuclear reactor from the contents of the average kitchen drawer.

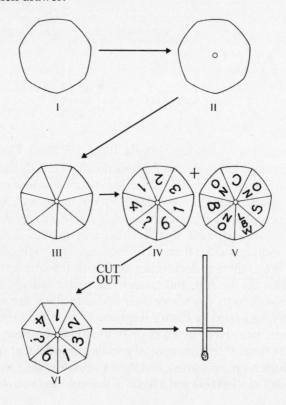

Garden Cricket

NATURE OR NURTURE? Tabula Rasa, or Total Genetic Pre-programming? Do we enter this world intellectually liveried, or as naked mentally as we are physically? Is our behaviour predestined by our parentage, or moulded by our mentors? Are we the products of our environment, or encoded by our precedents?

It is an argument that has raged in politics, religion, and education ever since there have been enough people on the planet for a few of them to decide they knew with absolute certainty what was best for the rest, and enough material surplus to allow them the leisure to try to enforce their decisions. How are we to attain heaven on earth? by Plato's Republic or Lenin's? Or our earthly rewards in heaven? by Faith or Works? How best can a child be taught to read? by grammatical grinding or indulgent osmosis?

Much more important, and the topic of this tale, can you take a boy with two left feet and a heart of soft gold and convert him into a top competitive cricketer with a killer instinct and an exquisite on-drive?

The answer is, quite simply, yes you can. I have seen it done, and you have probably applauded the product. Young Nairn-Oglethorpe is rapidly making a lot of runs at University, County, and Junior Representative level, and they tell me that he is widely tipped as a future England Test captain. They are probably right; they could do worse; they frequently have.

It could be that he is making a name for himself, but it would be more accurate to say his father made it for him, and now watches while the boy builds up a reputation to match it. Dad was just plain Hector Nairn. I grew up round the corner from his family home, and we played a lot together in our youth. Never cricket. In fact, never anything more muscular than Monopoly. Hector not only had the two left feet he handed on to his son, but his elbows seemed to be fixed on the wrong way round, and his Motor Coordination System worked on a purely random, or at best, long-term statistical basis. He was a tall, spindly child, with a big head, full of brain, and enormous shoes, full of the famous feet. He always seemed to be in the process of falling over, but he seldom actually did. I suppose it was because of the broad base provided by what Fats Waller would have called his 'Pedal Extremities' – they were certainly extreme.

He was deadly at any game long on luck and lucidity, and short on strength and physical skill. In our earliest days he used to wipe the board with me at Snakes and Ladders; with the years, we graduated through Ludo, Dominoes, and Draughts to Chess, and I don't remember taking a single game from him at any of them. He didn't even need to cheat, which in childrens' play was unnerving. I gather much of his later success in the business world has been due to this unusual combination of high intelligence, good fortune, and unexpected honesty.

He came from a humble home, but at thirteen he won a scholarship to a Scottish private school that modelled itself on the more admirable aspects of the English public variety, and I lost touch with him. We met up twenty years later when we found ourselves, married and with young families, once again just round the corner from each other, but now in exile in a Southern City.

He had fathered four girls and one boy. I don't think he worried very much about the girls; he loved them dearly, but they took after their mother in their good looks, and he reckoned that as long as they were decently clothed and not over-educated, they would marry happily and respectably, and give him many grand-children to cheer his old age in small doses. This is exactly what they have done, and at the last count the tally was twelve.

Hector wooed and won a lovely lass, largely for her looks and sweet disposition no doubt, but just marginally, I suspect, for her name. Not in the social-climbing sense, though she sprang from the cadet branch of a family famous for founding colonies and then losing them rather carelessly. Her maiden name was Oglethorpe, and it was Hector, not she, who insisted in retaining it in a double-barrelling which did not in any way reflect the circumstances surrounding their admittedly hasty nuptials. The son, when he arrived eventually fifth and last in line, was christ-ened Iain Osborne Oliphant, which may be fumbling phonetic-ally, but shortens symbolically into the prophetic initials I.O.O. N-O.

Hector brought away from his Anglo-Scottish school two very English passions; their indulgence gave him his fun and his fortune for the rest of his life. The first is that for dogs: he does not share it, but he exploited it by inventing a canine crunchie bar made from bits of coconut shells left over when everything else of use has been removed. I get the impression that he has cornered the market in this previously worthless commodity for the next ninety-nine years at a price agreed before the vendors knew it had any value, so as long as the English sprinkle copra on their curry, take dogs for muddy walks, and wipe their shoes when they return, he is on to a good thing.

The other Anglophile addiction has Hector hooked com-pletely. He cannot play cricket in any meaningful manner, but he is besotted by it, as a greybeard groom by a barely nubile bride. Apart from checking occasionally that the money is still pouring off the palm-trees (and the Registered Offices of Doggie-Dross Ltd are in Kennington, in order to cut down on time wasted on that chore), he spends his entire energy and time on cricket in general, and in particular on the promotion of his ambition to get his son playing in the highest levels of the game. Some critics carp at this, but I see no fault; many men invest their interest exhaustively in their children's careers. If they be academic, it is considered admirable; if professional, prudent; if in commerce, canny. Very few get more fun out of it than Hector Nairn, and the pleasure given to others by his son's flashing bat as he drives his way to the upper reaches is a public bonus seldom paid on family fantasies.

I remember well how his father was upset because Iain didn't seem to be able to get his stance quite right, and was only partly comforted when I assured him this was not uncommon at eighteen months. The best coaches were hired; the boy's nanny wore white flannel instead of the usual blue serge. He ended up with a good education accidentally because the school his father chose for him, famous for its sporting scholarships, placed as much stress on the scholarship as on the sport.

He learned most of his cricket in his own back garden; the lawn is almost exactly twenty-two yards long, with a short path leading straight up to the middle of one end, and a stout fence behind the other. I always think the house itself inadequate, considering the size of the family and their bank balance, but I don't suppose Hector would move even if they offered to build him a palace on the edge of the square at Lord's; he thinks his garden pitch plays as true as any in the land, and it doesn't have a ridge.

I and my growing family played a lot of cricket in the Nairn-O. garden, because we liked them a great deal and visited them often; you never came away from that household without having played cricket in some form or another, usually out in the back. Girls – theirs and any visiting – were used ruthlessly for fielding fodder. They seemed quite happy with this, when younger because it meant extra cakes for tea, later because it meant extra boys.

They always seemed to have two dogs, identical albino bullterriers; these spent all their lives doing two things extremely well – sleeping noisily in front of the fire, or fielding on either side of Hector, who couldn't catch anything faster than epidemic influenza. They would walk in with the bowler, beady red eyes fixed on the batsman, and anything more than half an inch off the ground passing within five feet of them was snapped up instantly. It was hard on the ball, but it got rid of many a batsman, taught Iain the virtue of all-along-the-ground driving, and made Hector feel like a Test match cover specialist, for custom credited him with whatever the dogs picked up.

Iain got his stance sorted out by about three and a half, and his two left feet much earlier than most boys, for his mother was a graceful and lissome woman, and he moved as she did, her control and beauty made masculine by muscle. She watched his progress with proud approval, and supported her husband's sporting passion with quiet enthusiasm. Like many women, she wanted adult virility in her men, but preferred to see it sublimated into childish channels most of the time, so that she could monitor it motheringly rather than have to respond to it as a sexual challenge or be dominated by it. She saw games merely as methods of keeping the babes of her brood (of all ages) out of mischief, and cricket as one of the better games because it is reasonably peaceful and lasts for hours. It has the drawback of being played in white clothing on grass, but they do stop for tea, and the ladies can get together for a bit of girl-talk over the sandwich-making. (Women in groups do not revert to girlishness in the way that men return to their childhood customs when they cluster; on such occasions it is not so much a matter of the crusts being subjected to feminine cutting as the company to feline shredding.)

Iain's cricketing development was dominated by the design of that garden, and you can see it reflected in his stroke-play to this day. Down one side of the lawn (the leg-side) there was a stretch of rhododendrons, sturdy bushes which could absorb a lot of punishment. So they got it, and as a result the lad built up a fine repertoire of strokes between square leg and mid-wicket. From mid-on to mid-off were the two terriers, so he hardly ever plays straight aggressively. On the off-side there was a long rose-bed, with a lone clump of azaleas about two-thirds of the way down. Mrs Nairn-O. didn't mind much what happened to most of the garden, but she liked a supply of fresh roses cut for the house, and by secateurs, not sliced drives. As a result, Iain plays a lovely forcing cover shot, off his front or back foot equally well, but

[125]

always through a narrow arc between wide mid-off and extra cover.

Just backward of square leg was a greenhouse, glass-fronted down to ground level, but only head-high. Beyond it stretched a tempting orchard, full of fruit trees and runs, but only safely reached with a lofted hook. This has made Iain particularly vulnerable to the mock bumper, bouncing juicily to chest height. It is the sort of chink in the armour that probing by a top-level captain opens up pretty quickly, and he is beginning to lose his wicket with dangerous regularity to catches deep at backward square. We all have gardens that we grew in, and they condition our behaviour for the rest of our lives if we let them.

The man who taught me most about quality cricket (I learned much about it but not how to play it) was a very useful left-hander who had captained his university, played for one of the County sides for a year or two, then moved north to teach full-time. While there, he joined a good club, and made huge quantities of runs opening for them, including a series of eleven centuries on consecutive Sundays. He then moved south again, to captain another County side; this he did brilliantly, lifting them in three seasons from the bottom of the championship to very near the top without a single change in players. It was a superb example of the value of good captaincy, but he didn't do it by making all the runs himself; in fact, for the first two seasons he had terrible trouble getting any sort of score, and the learned cricket columns were full of in-depth analyses of the onerous effect of office on personal performance.

The real reason, which he told me himself, was much simpler: his early cricket had been played on a narrow peninsular field at the bottom of his flowerbed-infested, dahlia-dominated garden. The field was about a hundred yards long, was bounded on three sides by a fast-flowing stream, and had a small shed about thirty yards in from the extreme end. His parents considered cricket cruelly combative; the slaughter of inedible fish they called angling, and approved. He and his brother therefore set their rods in full view of the house, and played single-wicket hidden by the hut.

This meant that the batsman always faced the stream, thirty

[126]

yards away in an arc from square leg to backward point. Forcing strokes in front of the wicket were therefore severely inhibited by the prospect of losing the ball, so he learned to turn practically every delivery into a tickle, glide, or steer backward of square. To do this with scoring success in real cricket, you have to be facing quick bowlers. As an opener he did, but when he took over the County captaincy there was already an established early order, which as an unproven batting quantity he did not dare disturb. He therefore had to put himself in at about No. 6, where he tended to meet the spinners. He couldn't score off them, so he couldn't prove himself as a batsman, so he didn't feel justified in moving himself up the order, so. . .

Luckily, he could pay for his place with his captaincy, but I can think of other young hopefuls who have been caught in similar or reverse traps and destroyed by them. Success at that level in sport is a matter of manipulating reality; lower down you can fashion fable into fun and favourable issue, or prosper through pretence. Even though it is well known in the circles in which I play that I cannot score off good length balls on middle-and-leg, and often get out to them, by the time anyone manages to bowl one at me there is a chance that I may have bludgeoned thirty quick runs; the chance is slim, but in a 20-over evening game that is a useful score, and if it happens four or fives times in a season I have justified my place in the side, and done enough to keep my dreams floating. In first-class cricket, if I ever reached such a level with such a handicap, it would soon be discovered, and every ball I faced would be of good length and bang on two legs.

I know of few more congenial ways of enlivening the shared observation of an innings of obvious technical limitation than reconstructing the childhood conditions which led to their development. The same method can provide much amusement if applied to minor idiosyncrasies; what Freudian episode can possibly have imposed that rather indelicate scratching with which one of our leading players celebrates the end of every over? Some friends of mine were once asked to leave the Members' Enclosure at a Famous Ground because of collective hysteria induced by a local competition to produce the most far-fetched but logical explanation of why a certain overseas bowler hitched up his trousers before each delivery in quite the manner he did.

Let us, however, return to the questions posed at the start of this discussion. Pliny the Elder said that man is the only animal that has to learn everything except how to weep. Old Pliny was a wise bird – it was he who observed that there is truth in wine, though presumably his local supermarket did not yet have on its shelves Real Dinkum Kangaroo Reisling in tubes – but this is an extreme view which exposes the pessimistic partiality which also led him to state that suicide is God's greatest gift to sorrowing humanity. Extreme solutions are by definition either hopelessly weak or revoltingly strong, and I suspect that the truth in this case lies, as usual, somewhere in the middle. Biologists put it very grandly by saying that 'the Phenotype is the product of the interaction between the Genotype and the Environment', which is one of those stunning sentences which have deep and precise meaning, but only if you know the language, which is not everyday English. Roughly translated, it means that we come into the world equipped with certain potentialities, but how we finally turn out depends on the manner in which they are exploited in our development.

If we apply this notion to Iain Nairn-Oglethorpe's cricket, the Nurture side of things is clear – he had the best there is. There is a naïve notion about that with proper training anyone can become a top sportsman; this is clearly and demonstrably false, though the clarity is clouded by the different but related point that more could reach the highest levels and the general standard could be raised significantly if better coaching and facilities were more widely available.

Where then, did his potential come from? His enthusiasm he got from his father, but that must have been imposed, in a benign sense, rather than inherited, for I doubt if there is a chromosome carrying cricketmania among our transmitted material. Most people assume that his intelligence comes from Dad too, but I would question this. Hector is certainly very bright, but on a high cerebral plane, which is not the level needed in cricket. What you need in order to do well in sport is a blend of commonsense and low cunning, both of which tend to flow more abundantly down the distaff side in most families.

We have already seen that Iain's muscular skill and coordinated movement must have come from his mother, but if he is to get to the very top and captain a Test side some time in the future, he will need one final attribute – a ruthlessness born of an urge to win willing to employ any available means not specifically denied by spirit or letter of law, and not too fussy about the spirit. Has he got it, latent within him?

When Iain was about fifteen, my son and I augmented the Nairn pack in a garden match against a posse of cousins and uncles from distant parts. There was some family point being proved and the needle was obviously in; the game, politely pleasant on the surface, was underneath being played out with deadly serious intent. We made a reasonable total before tea, but afterwards the cousins struck back firmly, and began to clock up the runs with alarming ease. Just about then Mrs Nairn-Oglethorpe wheeled out the big pram, complete with cat-net, which we were well used to seeing in that garden now that the grandchildren had begun mounting up; she placed it in its usual site at the far edge of the lawn, roughly at deep long-on.

Local rules in Garden Cricket accept prams without question as extra fielders, and this one had their three main scorers caught in the deep off Iain's rather useful donkey-drops within twenty minutes. That broke the back of their innings, and we duly won by a fair margin.

It was only when we got home that my son mentioned that neither of the then married daughters was staying in their old home that weekend.

There wasn't a single baby in the house.

Iain should have it all right – distaff side again.

Military Training Cricket

IT WAS NOT EASY to get twenty-four grown men into an old-style First Class railway compartment – the type off a corridor, four seats to a side with the armrests down, a table hinged onto the lower windowframe, resting at the other end on a single leg halfway down the space between the seats.

It was especially difficult if one of them was Ricky Bird in uniform. He was not all that large, five foot eight in his ammunition boots, fifteen stone of expensive flab oozing out on either side of his belt (webbing, khaki, officers, fat, too small for the use of). In the sense that a sphere is the most economic way of packing maximum volume into minimum surface area, I suppose you could even say that he was compact. Had we been travelling as civilians, eight or less to a compartment, he would have fitted very comfortably into one of the ample areas between the armrests, for railway companies have always allocated their First Class space in much the same way as most restaurants nowadays apportion their helpings – charging more than it is worth for more than you want.

The trouble was that, in his military mode, Ricky did not so much gird up his loins as truss up his entire topography. He was not equipped, he was festooned. On expeditions such as this he insisted on wearing a harness he had dug from deep in our stores, obsolete since Mafeking, which had hooks, clips and buckles on every conceivable position, and some in places apparently chosen to prevent conception. He found something to hang on every one: large packs, small packs, ammunition pouches ('Spare socks, of course'), bed-roll, groundsheet, gas-mask ('To deal with your lack of spare socks'), revolver-holster (empty), bayonet (blunt, used mainly as a tent-peg), bren-magazine pouches (each held a ten-pack carton as if designed for the job, which may well have been the case; it was certainly quite impossible to get a bren-magazine into one), spare barrel sling, bandolier, steel helmet, first aid kit, and a thing for purifying the water if the Fuzzy-Wuzzys dropped goats' entrails in the oasis.

On manoeuvres it was even worse: he looked, and sounded, like a walking Christmas tree, weapons and wirelesses sprouting from his person in profusion and all directions. He could be seen and heard for miles, day or night, and the best way of ensuring victory in a mock battle was to persuade him to act as Umpire-Observing-the-Other-Side. That way you knew exactly where they were at all times; this is terribly important in warfare, and is known as Intelligence. One of the virtues of the military mind is this insistence on acquiring factual information; its major vice is an obstinate refusal to base subsequent decisions logically upon it. The exact reverse obtains, of course, in politics, where most decrees derive through arguments of intellectual impeccability from funds of fabricated falsehood and inherited ignorance.

In open country Ricky was harmless, even useful as an early-warning system if you were on the other side; our hardware was primitive, but with him around, who needed radar? He was also completely safe, unless he moved too quickly and hit you with one of the bits of metal protruding from his animated arsenal; his mass/inertia coefficient ensured that this was an unlikely occurrence. None of the clutter he carried actually worked; no quarter-master would ever let him out with an intact radio, for he was the sort of man who has merely to touch a switch for it to come away in his hand with bits of wire and solder trailing, and in any case his normal speaking voice carried further than our sets even when they worked perfectly. Nor would any armourer issue him with a weapon that could actually fire anything: not even blanks, for they can kill at twenty yards, and we sometimes had to come closer to borrow cigarettes, and always eventually to divest him of his impedimenta – he could get it all on by himself, but it took three strong men to get it off.

Ricky was the Commanding Officer of our school Cadet Force; we were returning from Annual Camp; and he was mad keen on cricket. As in practically everything he did, a sort of madness was an essential ingredient, and gave his company the flavour that raised it above the usual social stodge to the heady level of Cordon Bleu. He was one of those rare beings, precious beyond price, who are superbly good at what they choose to do though slightly bonkers, or maybe because they are slightly bonkers. His classroom was like a circus, but boys would do anything for him; underneath the apparent chaos there was tight control, and his pupils acquired and retained an understanding and love for the subject which is the hallmark and ultimate reward of the good teacher.

He didn't play cricket all that well, but he didn't pretend to. He coached and organized it magnificently. His secret was that he looked on it as something to be enjoyed. Of course, you cannot enjoy it unless you play it in a disciplined way and to the best of your ability, but he was a true amateur in the sense that has nothing to do with money. He found sport, as he found life, far too full of fun to be treated as the be-all and end-all of existence. Those rolls of fat bulging by his belt would have been gross in their quivering had not the commonest cause of the quake been a chuckle. This attitude was backed by one of the best minds I have ever known, and had been reached through experiences that included a Military Cross won in the Burma Campaign and survival won from two years in a Japanese prison camp. What he never won was advancement, and at the time I wondered. Now, looking back, I am sure; in comparison with Ricky Bird, it was those who blocked him who were mad. He paid the inevitable price of laughing at pomposity and pretentiousness, but it bought him great respect and much love. Perhaps if more of us had the courage to share it, the total bill would gradually diminish.

Annual Camp that year was at Pinhearty in the West Country. It was what the Army called an Organized Camp, which meant that a large number of school contingents were sent to the same place, supervised by a retired regular officer; that way the chaos and damage were localized instead of being spread all over the countryside. In those days (they tell me all is now changed), the Services treated the Cadet Force as if it was a type of measles – something a developing fighting machine had to go through when young, but not anything that much need be done about, and best isolated from the rest of the community when at its most active.

We went by train; usually this meant a couple of tatty carriages tacked on to a scheduled service, but rendered shambolic by being the wrong service based on last year's schedules. Napoleon said, 'The most difficult feat a general can perform is to bring two armies from different places and join them on the battlefield as a single force against the enemy.'

He obviously had the same lot doing his transport arrangements as we did.

On this occasion the muddle was inverted. There were two contingents travelling from our area: 115 cadets and 22 officers. When we arrived at the station we found a complete twelve-carriage train specially laid on to take us direct to the railhead nearest to the camp. They were the latest Pullman carriages, too, with plastic carpets down the middle, plastic chintz curtains, dainty plastic antimacassars, and welded plastic tablecloths. Ricky noticed immediately that the carpeting was the same stuff he had seen being tested for indoor wickets at Lord's, and within twenty minutes he had the whole thing sorted out. The officers took over the two First Class carriages at the front end of the train; one became the pavilion, the other the pitch, and we began an epic match between our eleven and the officers from the other school.

We weren't really officers, though we held Commissions from

His Majesty printed on heavy-duty cream wallpaper. I never got beyond the stage of admiring mine and showing it to my close relatives, before I lost it, so I don't know the precise wording, but it probably authorized Our Well Beloved and Loyal Servant to play cowboys-and-indians every Wednesday afternoon and have a ten-day thrash at Our expense once per annum. It used to worry me a bit that I spent most of my working time poorly paid by one branch of the Government to instil in boys a love and understanding of life, and the rest overpaid by another branch teaching them how to destroy it. The worry was not burdensome, for I recognized that I performed the first job adequately, but the second with saving ineffectuality. In the meantime the cadets learned pieces of deep military wisdom such as: 'Never volunteer,' 'If it isn't screwed down, it's lost,' or 'If it moves, salute it; if it doesn't, paint it white.'

We had the cricket kit with us; during Troop Movements it was held under close care by the junior subaltern. Losing a rifle was theoretically a court-martial offence, but we reckoned that, had an officer lost the bats, Ricky would have shot him out of hand. He went so far once as to propose equipping the guarding officer with one of those chains that King's Messengers wore, the kind that buckle round the waist, run down inside the sleeve, and are padlocked on to the precious burden. We managed to persuade him that it would be unfair on the poor 2nd Lieutenant, for Ricky would most certainly have lost the key, and it would surely be hard to be permanently attached to a large scruffy bag clearly marked 'Reserve Pool "B" Series (Rejects)'. It must, however, be said that we once lost all the rifle-bolts and the RSM in a change of trains at Crewe; they and he failed to turn up until the last day of Camp, without any obvious effect on its smooth running, but I cannot think what we would have done if we had left the sports kit behind.

By the time the match began, the train was well under way, and we soon realized that regional rules would have to interpret international laws liberally. There looked to be a lot of runs in the wicket: flat as a billiard table, very firm surface, just a hint of green in it, it should have let the ball come through well and true on to the bat; just the sort of strip to encourage bold stroke-play. In an

Oval Test, it would have had the telegraph tripping over at a merry rate, 150 up before lunch and much toil in the field in prospect thereafter. The only trouble was, the Oval square isn't normally hurtling along a war-weary track at seventy-five miles per hour, bouncing around against the soles of the players' feet like a demented health machine designed to shake up a lowly liver or sink a floating kidney.

The problems we faced can be considered under three headings: batting, bowling, and fielding. That in itself suggests correctly that they were fairly comprehensive.

The passageway down the middle of a pullman carriage is remarkably narrow, as anyone can confirm who has ever struggled along it with two large suitcases, a screaming three-year old, a carry-cot, and a pregnant wife more or less in hand. From the point of view of batting technique, the constriction enforces to the point of absurdity that tendency induced by practice in narrow nets to play everything straight back to the bowler. In the confines of a carriage a straight bat is obligatory, the choices limited to forward or back, defence or attack. The frolicking floor underfoot had one advantage: it eliminated the classic error of too much right hand, for that had to be clamped firmly on to the nearest seat-back, and every stroke had to be attempted the way the paper experts tell us we ought to be able to play them if only we really tried – top hand only. Well, all of us there then tried, but none of us there then could.

The batting breakthrough came after almost half the long journey had passed with much fun, many bruises, and very few runs. The batsman in at the time played a straight drive with the blade accidentally reversed, and found that the ball skittered off at an angle, profitably among the seat-legs. I am not sure if this is actually against the letter of the law, but for this match it was instantly adopted as normal practice.

Another problem then became apparent: there just wasn't room for two batsmen to pass each other running between wickets, unless one of them used a space between seats as a sort of lay-by, which led to confusion and run-outs due to conditioned reflex courtesy. This was solved by having only one batsman at a time, who scored a single by running halfway down the carriage and back again. This is common procedure in Street Cricket, due not to trembling tarmacadam but a shortage of bats.

Bowling was, if anything, more difficult than batting; it was almost impossible until we discovered the necessary modifications of technique. The first ball was bowled off an eighteen-pace run by a young officer on the other side much fancied as a quickish seamer. His plan was to start at the far end of the pavilion carriage, build up his run as he accelerated down that passageway, get his left shoulder classically across as he hurtled through the link section (doors held open by very fine mid-off and -on), then deliver the ball from the bowling crease, which had been designated as an imaginary line through the rear legs of the second pair of seats from the door.

He did the first part remarkably well; it is very difficult to run freely along the corridor of a fast-moving, swaying train but by the time he got to the link section, he was moving pretty fast and with amazingly coordinated balance. What he forgot was that each carriage was running on a separate set of wheels, and so bounced and swayed in a completely independent rhythm to its neighbour. His front foot hit a floor that was moving in a direction totally different to what his brain was expecting, and he was flung violently off his stride and into the right-hand row of seats. A wooden armrest struck him a fearful blow on what was in the broadcasts of those days described as the Upper Thigh, and he collapsed on the plastic carpeting emitting a series of high-pitched squeaks and turning a particularly interesting shade of puce. He continued to speak in this upper register all the rest of the week, and I feared he had done himself a dynastically terminal injury, but anxious enquiry when he did not return to school the following term discovered that this had been his normal speaking voice, and that their headmaster had decided he was not entirely suited to the care of young boys for different but related reasons. From then on we bowled underhand, slowly.

Fielding was a matter of crawling about under the seats trying to find and dislodge the ball while the batsman scampered about a foot from your head and frequently over your legs. The main problems were broken fingernails, battered shins, torn trouser-knees, and top-to-bottom blacking, for in those days of steam a thick layer of grime from the smoke-stack filtered spontaneously into the carriages; nowadays, with the much cleaner diesel and electric engines, they have to invoke productivity agreements to get them into the traditional grubby state.

By the time we reached the railhead, the match was poised in a nicely balanced state. I don't recall the precise scores, but we were halfway through our reply to a fairly challenging total, holding our own, but only just. It could have gone either way: something like 90 for 5, chasing 140. The game was continued nightly in the mess, starting at about 2200 hours and carrying on until stumps were drawn by some very understanding and heavily tipped bar stewards at or around 0100. Unfortunately, mutual hospitality between the two contingents being at a lavish level, nobody at breakfast could remember very clearly the latter stages of the previous night's play, and those not at breakfast couldn't remember the previous night at all. It was therefore agreed that we would finish the match as it had begun, under Military Training Rules, on the way home.

We had to bus to the local station to start the return journey, and found to our horror that the planners had reverted to their usual mean-minded mismanagement after the beneficent bungling of the outward trip: we had been allocated one Third Class pullman carriage to take all 115 boys, and one First Class compartment in a corridor carriage for the 22 adults. This was not unusual; we were used to it, and it simply meant drawing up a rota, with most of us sitting on our luggage in the corridor, taking turns to have a spell on the comfortable seats in the compartment.

Most men would have accepted as inevitable that the circumstances spelt the cancellation of the match; not so Ricky. He showed his true leadership qualities, the sort that can lift men to such peaks of loyalty and enthusiasm that they will tackle patently pointless and suicidal assaults with songs in the hearts about to be shredded by shrapnel. Women are totally impervious to such appeals, which is why you never find them playing cricket on crowded trains.

Very shortly he had us all engaged in the game again, with the rules modified to a form of Table Cricket. As the name implies, this is played on table-top at a miniature scale. Methods vary, but

[137]

we used a small book standing on end as a set of stumps (the popular *Schoolboy's Diary* is ideal for this, as well as having an invaluable set of Illustrations of the Flags of the World in Full Colour). A pencil serves well as a bat: not a tooth-scarred scholar's stump, but the full-length virginal Venus all teachers have because they can pinch them from the box in the storeroom cupboard. There is much argument about grip: I have always found holding the pencil like a pencil the best method, but from the other end. We used a ping-pong ball, flicked with the knuckles as in marbles; I have known games where a billiard ball was used, but this tends to run through a lot of pencils and knuckles.

With all twenty-two players crowded into the compartment, plus two railway employees who came to collect tickets and stayed to umpire, we found it difficult to push the score along. The fielding side insisted that all of us had to be present, ostensibly to see fair play, partly because it was more fun, but mainly because they realized that it is a formidable task scoring sixes and fours when you cannot even see the boundary, never mind reach it. We had six seated on each bench (armrests up, of course), two draped along each luggage-rack, two standing against the door (the umpires), two crouched against the side windows, two lying along the floor, and, somewhere in there, the batsman and bowler.

The game continued in this manner for some time, constricted but not constrained, until Ricky himself ended it with the biggest and most expensive hit I have ever witnessed. We must have lost a few more wickets, for our captain never batted above No. 10, and the press of bodies and the heated hilarity had forced us to open the sliding bit of the window at the top to its fullest extent. The bowler tossed up a tempting thumb-spinner, Ricky lashed out at it, got a top edge, and sent it swirling out of the compartment.

There was a goods train passing at the time. We never saw the ball again, but Ricky claimed it as the longest hit ever because he says it was returned by the manager of Plymouth Power Station to Maybury-Smythe iii, a revolting meticulous boy from whom Ricky had confiscated it for trying to stuff it up Inskip's left nostril. It had written on it in tiny but clear lettering the usually un-answered schoolboy pleas:

If I wander send me home

To   J.J.T. Maybury-Smythe,
                Singer's House,
                St Bede's School,
                Pootersfield Park,
                Nr Luton,
                Bedfordshire,
                England,
                Great Britain,
                The World,
                The Solar System,
                The Universe

How he got all that on to a ping-pong ball I do not understand, but as he went on to a successful and highly paid career designing bank-notes (legally, for the Bank of England) I cannot question his capability.

I am inclined to accept Ricky's claim. Some years ago there was a Reverend Gentleman who stated that, when playing for his prep school, he had struck a ball over long-on and the hedge bordering the Grand Union Canal. It there lodged in the chimney of a barge carrying coals to Newcastle, whence it was returned, freshly laundered, by a fellow-cleric; his washer-woman had picked it up while searching for slack, and he recognized the crest embossed on the leather. Since the school was situated near Dunstable, the tale, though economically unlikely, is physically possible, and it is against my nature to doubt the word of a man of the cloth; the fabric of our society rests on the reliability of such strands, and I do not believe in weakening it, even with doses of strong bleach.

Why did Ricky's shot end the game, and why so expensively?

Their captain was a Wing-Commander, and the Junior Service is, I suppose, accustomed to long-range, stand-off combat, rather than the hurly-burly of the hand-to-hand stuff, but when that ball went through the window, and both luggage-racks collapsed as fielders dived for it, he panicked. I'm sorry, but there is no other word for it. As they say nowadays he lost his cool, and about £80 in fines and damages.

He pulled the communication cord.

Granny Cricket

GRANNY CRICKET is dead.

She passed away peacefully, in her sleep, last Friday night; George Dunwoody sent me the clipping from *The Scotsman:*

MACLEOD, Fiona Mary; aged 101; at her home in Burnbrae, Bingshire. . . . . . . 'at Rest'.

'At rest'? Stuff and nonsense! as Granny herself would have said, probably still is saying. 'Doing nothing is just such awful hard work' was how she replied, right to the end, to those who suggested she should take her ease a bit more. It was amazing how, at her great age, creaking at every joint, bent like a letter C, walking only with the support of a frame, she nonetheless managed to give a shaming impression of energetic bustle as she found things to tidy away whose displacement no one else had noticed.

I suppose she could be reckoned to be of little account; her passing will not be noticed by many, certainly not by many in her own little town. Her near neighbours knew her as a close old buddie with a sharp tongue who read strange foreign newspapers like *The Times* and *The Observer*, kept herself to herself, and had lived in No. 82 for ever.

Outsiders came to visit her from outlandish places: Edinburgh, Hawick, Birmingham, London even, and once a car with American Embassy plates on the back. Corpse Dipsomaniac, no less! They did not quite beat a path to her door, but there was a regular trickle, and it was surprising how often people with no other regular links met up when visiting Granny Cricket, people from all walks of life, and seldom walking, either; these were successful people. Successful in a minor, happy way, like the schoolmaster in his secondhand Volkswagen, ranging right up to successful in a major, miserable manner – the pop-star in her rainbow-striped Rolls. We were all escapees; by means of education, drive, talent, or often just plain luck we had managed to break away from that mean and narrow environment, and although some may have felt pangs of guilt at being the recipients of random and selective good fortune, not one was touched by any trace of the regret for a lost culture movingly described in so many novels. Any culture that may have existed in the community had died long before we grew up within it; it was a depressed, ugly place, in more ways than the material, and none of us would ever have gone back if it had not been to see Granny Cricket.

We were all treated by her in exactly the same way – as if we were the wee lads and lassies she had known, and whom we knew ourselves, in some ways, still to be. We got keen interest in our doings, a humbling lack of awe over what we might in our vanity have thought impressive, an equal accolade for advance at whatever level, great or small. I have watched a young nurse thrill with excitement as Granny handed her the due reward for her promotion to Theatre Sister, while next to her sat a Minister of the Crown blushing in anticipation of his identical tribute for gaining a seat in the Cabinet – a large and extremely sticky piece of her home-made treacle toffee. He got it, of course, plus an enquiry about his 'wee wifey' (a society matron of massive influence and matching physical dimensions), and an urgent injunction to both of them not to leave off their warm woolly vests until the end of May.

When we left, each of us always got a parting gift 'to see us doon the road', always the same, a paper poke of Granny's toffee and a big shiny apple, and I remember walking down that street, aged the heavier side of forty-five, sticky bag in one hand, apple in the other, feeling for a few more magical moments as if I were once again on the carefree edge of ten.

To be strictly accurate, Mrs MacLeod was not really a granny at all. She had left her Hebridean home at fourteen; it was an island rich in natural beauty, but desperately poor in work or prospects for its young people, and she was forced to follow the footsteps of many before her, into domestic service in London. She was a parlour-maid to a middle-class professional family at fifteen, at seventeen married the local bobby, who came from her neighbouring island, bore him boy-twins the next year, and stayed in service as a daily assistant cook in one of the grand houses in Mayfair, until all the telegrams came in the same delivery on a terrible day of November 1917, telling her that the mud of Passchendaele had swallowed up her three fine men. Desolate, she came to live with a married sister in that then thriving mining village, and for a variety of reasons which I never fully understood, there she stayed till her death the other day.

But although she could claim no continuity in the flesh into future generations, spiritually she stretched out through the third and even into the fourth, for boys and girls had begun to call her Granny way back in 1920. She loved children, and until she grew too feeble physically to handle them on her own, delighted in having them around her. She would entice them into her little house, not with gingerbread, but with trays of what we used to call 'tablet', which I have now learned to ask for as 'fudge'. I accept this is an apt name, for I suspect that her fudge was toffee on a bad day.

She did not like children just because they were children. She was no soppy sentimentalist, and gave tender tolerance rather than enjoyment to juvenilia. She looked for potential, encouraged enlargement, pushed the world in our faces, tried to widen us with awareness. She wasn't really interested in what was happening in the immediate vicinity; local gossip bored her and, not unreasonably, this separated her from those who lived around her. She read a great deal, until her eyes failed (which was not until the last two years), in the classics, in contemporary literature, and in the press, and she was an avid listener to the 'wireless'. This, together with her talks to her visitors, made her one of the most informed people I knew – the girl who brought the 'Library-on-Wheels' round kept coming even after Mrs MacLeod stopped borrowing because of her blindness, 'For the sake' as she said, 'of my own education'. She may not have built the ships from her own raw material, but she certainly gave them the push that launched them out into the wide open sea.

Granny Cricket would entertain us for hours with tales from her days in service among the 'great' in the capital, and they bore little relation to the bowdlerized nonsense purveyed in popular novels and sycophantic memoirs. She could not be bothered with the new-fangled television, finding it too far removed from the written word, and thus, by her definition, the Truth, but we once brought in a set to let her see an episode of a series about life above and below stairs in Edwardian London; she nearly had a seizure laughing at it, but at the absurdity, not the intended humour. She had no time for those who decried the decline in moral standards among the youth of today, and could always cap any sensational scandal in the current gutter press with something much juicier from regions well above the gutters of pre-First World War London High Society. She had no illusions about the elevated tone of the upper crust, knowing that it was merely basted with a richer sauce than was available to humbler pies; it had a brighter gloss, but the corruption seethed more violently beneath. Good old Granny kept marvellously in touch with contemporary seething, too, and many an obscure and puzzling report in the press took on a new and fuller meaning when she filled in the background. She was a sort of 'Northern Spectator', with a network of reporters in key places, and, perhaps fortunately, a limited distribution.

A wonderful lady.

Well, she's gone now, and I shall miss her, and her talk, and her toffee, and her good clear Highland commonsense, and her gift for making me feel very young and very special. But why write about her here? We called her Granny Cricket because of her tiny stature and high chirpy voice, not for any connection with the game. There was no such connection, not that we knew of, or would have begun to imagine, for she had no interest in sport, except as one of the normal healthy activities of the young.

I saw her last in August, she was obviously failing, but still articulate. The company was discussing the English National Obsession. I think the last words she addressed to me fit well here:

'Cricket? Cricket, you say?'

'Yes, I heard you; no need to shout.'

Long pause.

'My first Gentleman was a great one for that . . . for the cricket.'
Another pause.

'Always at it . . . travelled a lot too . . . playing it, I think . . . or so he said . . . I could tell you a thing or t . . .'

I thought she had dozed off.

'Fine strapping man he was . . . that great bushy set of whiskers.'

A long, long gap; I began to gather myself to go.

'Don't know how he found the time . . . Medical gentleman, you know.'

She slept.